The Parish Nurse

*How to start a Parish Nurse Program
in your church*

by

*Granger E. Westberg
with Jill Westberg McNamara*

DEDICATION

This booklet is dedicated to the hundreds of thousands of nurses who have been drawn to nursing by the spirit and aims of the Great Physician. They have challenged the world of scientific medicine to take a greater interest in the spiritual dimension of health care.

In *The Parish Nurse* we respond to this challenge by offering unique opportunities for nurses who are so motivated. This congregationally-centered program calls forth a deeply spiritual concern for the whole person. Nurses who are involved in the parish nurse project say that it has the potential for transforming the nurse into a "Minister of Health."

The eight nurses in the Lutheran General Hospital sponsored
Parish Nurse program in the Chicago area

Lois Coldewey, RN
Luth. Ch. of Atonement
Barrington, IL

Saralea Holstrom, RN
Our Savior's Luth. Ch.
Naperville, IL

Mary Kay Frazier, RN
St. Raymond Cath. Ch.
Mt. Prospect, IL

Joan Linden, RN
Grace Lutheran Ch.
La Grange, IL

Sally McCarthy, RN
Our Lady of Ransom
Cath. Ch.
Niles, IL

Laura Reichert, RN
First United
Methodist Ch.
Park Ridge, IL

Susan Monaco, RN
Visitation Cath. Ch.
Elmhurst, IL

Marilyn Belleau, RN
Glenview Community Ch.
Glenview, IL

First Edition January, 1987

Printed in the U.S.A.

Distributed by
Parish Nurse Resource Center
Parkside Center
1875 Dempster St.
Park Ridge, Illinois 60068

TABLE OF CONTENTS

THE PARISH NURSE

How to start a parish nurse program in your church:

INTRODUCTION

For some forty years my professional life as a clergyman has centered around medical schools and teaching and research hospitals. As a faculty member I have seen the need for a whole-person approach to the problems of every patient. But the spiritual dimension of the person has generally been neglected in the scientific environment.

This neglect has bothered me. I have felt that it is not fair to the patients, all of whom have God-given souls which greatly affect the functioning of their bodies. Scientific medicine by overlooking that unique interaction has cheated the patients out of full-patient care.

There is now a new kind of humility among a growing number of leaders in the medical field. They recognize that something has been missing in their care of sick people. I think that now is the time for the rich resources of the Christian faith to be harnessed with the marvelous discoveries of modern medicine. Progressive leaders in both medicine and the church have their work cut out for them.

This Parish Nurse project, which is the theme of this writing, is one small attempt in the area of preventive medicine to show what can happen when a "nurse-in-the-church" stimulates the dialogue between science and religion at the grass-roots level.

Granger E. Westberg

Granger E. Westberg

Chapter One

A BRIEF SKETCH OF THE PARISH NURSE PROJECT

This booklet is meant to be of help to lay people and pastors of congregations who have long cherished the hope that their churches might minister more effectively to the needs of the whole person. I will be describing an action-research project which places nurses on the staffs of congregations as "ministers of health" to work alongside pastors and others who are dedicated to a wholistic ministry.

At the present time there is a great deal of interest in health and whole person theology. The Scriptures of the Judeo-Christian faith have much to say about the importance of the interrelationship of the body and the soul. And Jesus, when he sent out his disciples, made it clear to them that they were to be concerned about both the body and the soul. His command to them was, "Go, preach the kingdom of God and heal the sick."

The parish nurse project has been brought into being by many active lay people and clergy who are determined to follow Christ's command to heal as well as to teach and preach. They feel that such a unified ministry can be carried out in local congregations. How the healing or caring aspects of the church's ministry will develop remains to be seen. Those parish nurses* who are already involved in this important mission are discovering new ways to bring body and soul together.

The media is bombarding us with stories dealing with such topics as preventive medicine, self-care, stress-management, exercise and the interrelation of body, mind and spirit. We are impressed with much of what we read and hear, but applying the wisdom of a magazine article to our lives can be difficult. Some of the time we succeed. It might be though that we need a support group to deal with such whole-person problems, but we don't know where to turn to find such help. Most often we are well-meaning in wanting to bring about some changes in our lives, but we never quite get around to it.

How do we go about increasing the motivation we need to get us to change our unhealthy habits of living? And what does all this have to do with religion?

(*All our present parish nurses are women, so we will use the pronoun "she," but soon we hope that male nurses will join our ranks.)

7

I personally believe that our motivation for a serious life change has its roots in a person's outlook on life. By outlook on life I would, of course, be referring to a person's philosophy of life, belief system or faith stance. This immediately brings us into the realm of religion, for religion asks questions like: "Why are you so dissatisfied with your present style of life that you want to change it?" "Do you sense that there is more to life than you are presently experiencing?"

The question which physicians raise in any discussion with clergy is, "How can we motivate our patients to want to change their unhealthy life styles?" We know that very few people go out of their way to seek preventive health care. If motivation is intimately tied up with a person's way of looking at life, then it follows that perhaps it would strengthen one's motivational powers to be in the company of like-minded people who believe additional energy is available through spiritual commitment.

A parish nurse who does her caring for people within the community of faith just might offer such needed inspiration and this is perhaps why these parish nurses are often referred to as "ministers of health."

In churches across the country there is much going on that is helping people stay well — regular opportunities for building friendships, experiencing help through prayer and worship, opportunities to sing, to study, to serve others and, in turn, to be served by others. All of these things assist in creating an attitude of gratitude and hope which are known to contribute to health.

I now know of a growing number of churches which are becoming more intentional about being seen as centers to which people can turn for health care with a spiritual dimension. These churches are asking how they can help bring about a climate conducive to wholistic living. My experiences with parish nurses over a period of three years convinces me that the presence of a spiritually mature nurse on a church staff contributes greatly to clarifying the interrelationship of faith and health.

By calling a nurse to serve as a minister of health for a congregation, I have learned that people's health care needs can be responded to very effectively. We have observed each of our parish nurses as she has developed her role uniquely to fit that congregation's particular needs. Generally though, her role included the following areas of ministry:

1. *Health Educator:* The nurse teaches, or brings in others to lead, courses, seminars and workshops for the congregation

on a wide variety of health related topics such as, health maintenance, disease prevention, early detection through screening, the role of emotions in illness, and most important, an introduction to the interrelation of body and soul. Nurses in our project believe that "as one thinketh in one's heart, so does one's body tend to respond."

2. *Personal Health Counselor:* Primarily with members of the congregation, but also with some non-members, the nurse, a) provides a professional listening ear, b) does assessments of health problems, c) recommends and/or provides minor health care measures, or refers the person to a physician and/or community support services, as needed, d) educates individuals in specific ways that they might better care for themselves and communicate good health concepts as a role model.

3. *Trainer of Volunteers:* One of the nurse's roles is to find those women and men in the congregation who are just naturally warm, understanding persons who are willing to listen to people who are hurting. These volunteers can be instructed to do even better what they are already doing naturally. They then become additional hands, ears and eyes for the nurse as they make house calls on the sick, serve as small group study leaders and participate in many other tasks. In large congregations the nurse by herself cannot begin to respond to all the needs, so trained volunteers can add tremendously to her effectiveness.

4. *Organizer of Support Groups:* The nurse organizes and finds facilitators (possibly herself) for groups centered around particular issues such as weight loss, diabetes, divorce, stress management, arthritis, youth problems, problems of loss and grief, children of aging parents, etc.

We feel that because the nurse has her office in this unusual place called a church, special kinds of things can happen. It gives people easy access to a qualified health provider, encourages people to come in and talk about their human problems along with their "smaller" physical problems which often indicate early cries for help, encourages them to see their doctor sooner when the nurse senses that the problem has medical implications, and reminds people that the Church is interested in whole persons —mind, spirit *and* body.

The parish nurse takes time to listen, to counsel, to pray with people and to introduce them to small support groups. She represents an exciting new development for ministry in the congregation.

9

In our experimental project we have had no difficulty finding unusually qualified women who are spiritually mature. Their ability to move easily into many different kinds of caring situations within the congregation has convinced many church members that the parish nurse's talents add a necessary dimension to the ministry of the local church.

This booklet grows out of almost three years of experimental models in Tucson, Arizona, Sioux City and Des Moines, Iowa, San Jose, California, and Chicago, Illinois. Lutheran General Hospital in Park Ridge, Illinois, a northwest suburb of Chicago, has underwritten the major action-research project in the Chicago area. It has been a joint effort of the divisions of Nursing and Pastoral Care of that hospital.

The Lutheran General Hospital Program is related to eight suburban churches. Five are Protestant churches, with seven hundred to two-thousand members, and three are Catholic churches with eight to ten-thousand members. We chose these upper middle income area churches because of the expense involved in getting such a program under way.

Already the nuns of three Catholic hospitals in low income neighborhoods of the inner city of Chicago have become intrigued by the parish nurse project. They have employed a full-time chaplain, who was a theological student observer connected with the Lutheran General Hospital program, to be the coordinator of a project in several churches near those hospitals. Because these congregations could never afford to pay the salaries of these nurses, the hospitals bear the entire financial responsibility.

There are soon to be twenty churches in the greater Chicago area engaged in our parish nurse program. They represent churches from all income levels, high, middle and low, and include many of the minority and ethnic groups which make up Chicago's population.

In each city or town there are variations in the way the parish nurse program can be organized. Each congregation is free to structure its program in a way that best suits its needs, and much depends upon the quality of nurses who are available to work for a salary on a part-time basis, or as a volunteer.

In Tucson, Arizona, our first experimental congregation, the person who heads up the health clinic in the church is employed half-time on a salary by members and friends of the congregation. She is also employed the other half-time in Green Valley, a retirement town 25 miles away, at another church health center.

10

In Sioux City, Iowa area there are several congregations who have nurses who are members working part-time as volunteers. Some give an afternoon or an evening a week. Some give considerably more time than that. One is a nurse who gives every Monday afternoon to her rural church in a community where there are no physicians within 20 miles. She is the only health professional in the entire county.

In the San Jose, California area a growing number of churches have nurses who give from three to five hours a week as volunteer parish nurses. Some churches have three or four nurses in their membership who give approximately four hours each per week.

The Lutheran General Hospital Parish Nurse Program was structured as a half-time position with a salary of $10,000 a year, plus benefits. Each parish nurse employed by the Hospital is automatically included in its usual half-time benefit package. Over a three year introductory period, each of the eight churches pays an increasing percentage of the salary to the hospital. By the end of the third year, each congregation will be paying the entire salary. Some of the congregations have indicated a desire to have the nurse gradually move toward a full-time position.

At Iowa Lutheran Hospital in Des Moines a quite unique Minister of Health/Parish Nurse project is underway. Chaplain David F. Carlson who heads up that program stresses that the project will be aimed at what he calls a "pastoral model" rather than a "medical model." This experience-based education program is one year in length.

It begins with three weeks of intensive clinical pastoral education at the hospital, followed by an internship in a congregation(s). During the internship the Minister of Health candidate returns at regular intervals to Iowa Lutheran Hospital for seminars and collegial interchange. The curriculum content will seek to develop competencies in pastoral care, community health nursing, wholistic health and wellness, psychosocial concepts, assertiveness training and marketing and salesmanship. (See Appendix A)

St. Francis Hospital, a Catholic hospital neighboring Lutheran General Hospital, has also developed a program entitled, "The Parish Nurse Minister." The financial arrangements during the first year calls for the hospital to assume 75% of the parish nurse salary with the parish assuming 25%. During the second year, the parish covers one-half and the third year, three-fourths. The hospital continues the coverage for malpractice insurance and benefits.

11

Although the working arrangements may be different, the concept is the same. Health is being understood to include more than physical health and the interplay between the body, mind and spirit is looked at wholistically. The nurse is seen as a key part of the church staff in actualizing this concept.

Chapter Two

WHY A NURSE ON A CHURCH STAFF?

If a pollster were to knock on the doors of homes in almost any community and ask the question, "What are the health agencies in this community?" what answer would the pollster get? Most people would probably give the name of a local hospital and perhaps some well-known medical clinic. People naturally equate health care with hospitals and doctors.

But now the word "health" is taking on characteristics related to more than just "sickness care." It is not enough to mention only hospitals and doctors who generally spend most of their time taking care of people *after* they become sick.

Nurses have long been concerned about this over-accent on sickness care. Many have moved out into the community, away from hospitals, seeking to find ways to prevent people from becoming ill. They have frequently expressed the feeling that perhaps a third of the patients they have seen in hospitals over the past fifty years would not have become *that* sick if someone out in the community had been sensitive to their earlier cries for help. And many of these early symptoms at that point would have been reversible.

As a minister, I have had an unusual career because my life has been so closely related to the nursing profession. I started out as a parish pastor in the university community of Bloomington, Illinois, then chanced to spend a week as chaplain in a large Chicago hospital. I lived with residents and interns. I got less sleep and drank more coffee than any week of my life as the doctors and nurses got me involved in every conceivable human situation.

That one week experience changed my life. Three years later I became the first full-time chaplain of that hospital, and the first chaplain under 70 years of age. I was 30. For eight years I taught several hours a week in the school of nursing of that hospital and we developed the case study method of teaching the relationship of religion and health.

Then out of the blue came a call to joint professorship in Religion and Health at the University of Chicago Medical School and Divinity School. We soon inaugurated a weekly Religion-Medicine Case Conference over a Thursday noon brown bag lunch. A patient's current problem was presented by the patient's attending physician and resident, a nurse who knew the patient well and one of the hospital student chaplains who had ministered to the patient. This triumvirate of doctor, nurse and pastor symbolized for me a type of patient care I had always dreamed about. The conferences were attended by students in nursing, medicine and theology. Usually there were 10 to 30 people present. The intention of the conference was to take a serious look at the spiritual dimensions of the patient's illness and begin the necessary dialogue between these three professions which had so much in common. Some doctors went away from the conference scratching their heads and saying, "How did they get me involved in this unscientific approach to illness?" But others said, "This is the first time I have ever even thought about the religious dimension of my patients' illnesses. And it's the first time I've ever sat down on equal footing with nurses and ministers and had to slug it out with them!" And nurses said, "This is what ought to happen every day on the floors." They kept urging me to expand the concept.

The conference convinced a number of people that illness is a multidimensional phenomenon and that the fragmentation of the patient is one of our greatest problems.

After 12 years in a highly structured teaching and research hospital setting where we were seeing only very sick people, I began thinking over what nurses had been saying about the one-third of these patients who, if their illnesses had been detected earlier, would not have needed to become so ill.

Nurses convinced me that the field of preventive medicine would never go anywhere if it were to remain only in the hands of physicians. Many other professions and skills were needed including parish clergy who see people on a regular basis and often in informal settings.

Eventually I moved to the Department of Preventive Medicine of the University of Illinois College of Medicine. Through the encouragement of the W.K. Kellogg Foundation we eventually set up a dozen experimental family doctors' offices in church buildings where a team of doctor, nurse and pastor saw patients in a joint approach. These many Wholistic Health Centers have become teaching centers for literally hundreds of physicians, nurses and pastors from all over the country and a number from abroad. The evaluation of the project by outside observers indicates that they hope we will continue to operate these non-profit doctors' offices as demonstration projects. They particularly appreciated the openness on the part of the several staffs to creative ways of dealing with the whole patient. They saw the nurses as catalysts in getting medicine and theology to talk to each other. Nurses

14

seemed to have one foot in the humanities and one foot in the sciences, and thereby bridge the unnecessary gap between these two very old and esteemed professions.

Now we are expanding this wholistic concept hopefully into hundreds of congregations across America and Canada. The specific work of the nurses varies according to the setting of a given church. The primary thrust of the nurses' work is to identify the early cries for help and intervene before problems require hospitalization. The nurses, therefore, are doing most of their work in the areas of prevention and wellness. Through seminars, workshops, discussion groups and Sunday School classes they help individuals understand that health care is a part of the stewardship of one's life. With this in mind, it is the role of the nurses to involve people in their own health care and in the care of their neighbors. As people work together toward health, the load for the individual is lightened.

When I visited with parish pastors about the parish nurse project they showed greater interest in having nurses on their staffs than I expected. Pastors spend so much of their time calling on sick parishioners with whom, at times, they feel frustrated and inadequate to deal in a more wholistic manner. They say, "Perhaps we could team up in some kind of total patient care and see results we are not seeing now." One said, "I feel all alone ministering to some of these difficult people. I seldom can get doctors to talk over problems, but I've always had excellent relationships with nurses in my hospital calling. Maybe this would be the answer in my parish work."

Nurses have been serving people in this same spirit, touching people and then talking with them, often on a very deep level. That is exactly what is needed in every congregation, a balance between touching and talking or communicating. Without the touch the talking does not carry much power.

Clergy are more open to ideas related to health and wholeness because everything they have tried to say about the value of living a healthy, balanced life is now being certified, verified, and clarified by the research going on in the health sciences. To have a nurse as a representative of the health sciences on the church staff is to symbolize this close tie between one's faith and one's health.

And so we return to the question, "What are the health agencies in our communities?" If hospitals and doctors spend the majority of their time with people *after* they get sick, then what institutions of our culture help us to stay well? There are five, at least: the home, the school, the church (and other voluntary organizations),

15

the workplace and the public health department. If these five are in good shape we are very fortunate. If any one of them is not doing its job then we all begin to feel unwell.

A final word about the church as one of these institutions that deals more in wellness than in sickness. I am aware that there are some churches that make people sick. But I think they are in the minority. Most healthy churches offer a marvelous variety of interest groups, social activities, music, drama, discussion groups, and ongoing educational opportunities for age groups from the cradle to the grave. The parish nurse can add a dimension to their activities which is missing. Her task will be to prepare the congregation for its role in preventive medicine, in helping people understand the ingredients of the full, rounded life.

Much of what I am saying about collaboration between clergy and nurse is based upon my own experience of many years working alongside nurses. They have stood back of me during my tug-of-war with doctors who could not understand why the hospital should bother to have a chaplain. Nurses knew what I was going through because they themselves had been thwarted so long in their efforts to bring about changes in patient care. They longed to be creative in developing new and improved methods of teaching and relating to patients but were told that there was no time for such things. Long before anyone wrote articles on wholeness, wellness and prevention, nurses were already practicing whole-person-care — at least for the few moments they were allowed to escape from the technical aspects of their work.

For me, nurses are a national treasure, a reservoir, a pearl of great price which has been hidden in the field. Nurses have been pleading with the medical profession for 40 years to become more preventive-medicine oriented — to teach people how to stay well. Now is their chance to reach thousands of people in the informal setting of an institution which is ready to rethink its role in motivating people to healthy living.

16

Chapter Three

EIGHT STEPS TO A PARISH NURSE PROGRAM

STEP ONE

LEARN ALL YOU CAN ABOUT THE PROGRAM

If you would like to have a parish nurse as the minister of health for your congregation then you will want to familiarize yourself with as much background information as you can find. As yet there is not much written specifically dealing with the parish nurse concept. The best thing for you to do would be to meet with nurses, pastors and lay people who are already participating in a parish nurse project in their church. But not many of you live near those places. Information regarding who these congregations are can be received through the Parish Nurse Resource Center.

While you are waiting for more articles to be written on the subject, we hope this first edition of the HANDBOOK will answer many of your questions. Let's start with a few suggestions:

1. As you read this text, always keep in mind how its contents would or would not relate to your situation. No two churches are alike and no two nurses are alike. Allow for a great deal of flexibility in the style your health ministry may take.

2. Share this text with several other people and arrange for whole evenings of discussion.

3. Become acquainted with articles in newspapers and magazines as well as medical and nursing journals dealing with new concepts in preventive medicine and wellness care. The parish program is essentially concerned with how to keep people well.

4. Brainstorm with like-minded friends (include some medical professionals in this small group) concerning how this might work specifically in your church and in your neighborhood or town. No doubt they will be able to see some additional possibilities as well as stumbling blocks of which you were not aware. Assuming your friends show appreciation for the idea it might help to do an informal needs assessment together to

help determine the direction this project should take in your church.

5. Begin to think about the kind of nurse you are looking for because her abilities will set the pattern for the program. The basic requirement should be a registered nurse who, if possible, has a baccalaureate degree. But from that point on much depends upon the human and spiritual quality of this person; her ability to relate warmly to all kinds of people and what she has learned from previous professional jobs. Public health, school nursing and psychiatric nursing come to mind as helpful background, but several of our successful parish nurses have had med-surgical, oncology or pediatric experience. Who the person is, is more important than the specific kinds of job experience or education they have had.

6. Generally, parish nurses do not give "hands-on" care. We are trying to develop a style of nursing care unlike any other because of its teaching and spiritual dimensions. If there are physicians available, we think it is best, at our present stage of development, to refer people with strictly medical needs to a physician. However, in a rural area where the nearest doctor may be twenty or more miles away, we suggest the selection of a parish nurse who is a nurse practitioner.

STEP TWO

COMMUNICATE WITH THE PASTOR

Assuming that you are not the pastor of your church, then the pastor is the most significant person whom you must meet with at the beginning of your journey. If the pastor is not interested in the idea, then there is little hope of success. Therefore, the presentation of the concept to your pastor is of utmost importance.

Experience has shown that if only one person approaches the pastor the project can be very easily dismissed as "too difficult to tackle at the present time." But, if a group who have thoroughly studied the concept make a special appointment to see the pastor, it will be seen as a much more serious proposal. If this group can include a physician, then the idea cannot be easily dismissed.

And so, before you meet with the pastor you need to find the people who can give impetus to your efforts. Choose people whom you have found to be receptive in your earlier conversations and highly regarded in the congregation. Maybe their own work or life

18

experience has demonstrated the need for prevention and dealing with the whole person. As for finding nurses, most congregations have at least two or three members who are now, or in the past have been, active in nursing. In larger churches it often comes as a surprise to discover how many nurses are on the roll. In my experience nurses in the congregation have been the best supporters for this concept.

When you make your presentation to your pastor be sure you are well prepared to back up your statements with facts from the experience of congregations that now have parish nurse programs. Perhaps one person can present the over-all picture and other group members can deal with individual concerns.

Many pastors will almost immediately begin to describe situations in their congregations where a nurse could have been of real assistance.

The pastor who chooses to back the idea as a possible project for the congregation now has a key role to play in all future developments. The pastor can:

1. Provide a leading support for the project both within the congregation and in the community at large.
2. Assist in selecting supportive members of the congregation to work with an exploratory task force.
3. Help the original group to get the message to the people of the congregation.
4. Help select and contact other pastors in the community who might be interested in a community sponsored parish nurse project to be conducted in several congregations.
5. Undergird the project with Biblical foundations for whole-person health care to be found in both the Old and New Testaments.

STEP THREE

EDUCATE THE CONGREGATION

It is now time to involve a wider group of people in the process. This is the point when a task force can be very helpful particularly if they have been chosen from a cross-section of the membership.

Who should tell the story? Whenever presentations are made to groups and committees in the church, it is well to have two or three presenters who have done their "homework". Audiences always like to hear several points of view on a matter they will be asked to help sponsor.

You will find yourself telling this story over and over, not only to various organizations within the church, but also to individuals who have heard something about it, but do not have the facts straight. Remember that it is a radical idea to suggest that a congregation should actually become involved in health care. Why in the world would a church want to have a nurse, of all people, on the staff? For centuries we have separated health care and spiritual care to the extent that there has been no real communication between the two. The time is now ripe for the communication to begin.

To bolster your confidence, start with a group that will almost assure your sucesss — nurses. Invite all the nurses from your congregation (and perhaps others) to an evening of discussion of this project. The response has uniformly been one of gratitude that somebody is finally recognizing the potential of nurses in the area of preventive medicine and health education.

After meeting with the nurses, arrange to make presentations to the church. Do not overlook women's circles and men's groups. Encourage your task force members to be present at coffee hours where they can informally listen to the kinds of questions people are raising.

When the task force and the pastor think the time is ripe to present the parish nurse proposal to the official board of the church, ask for an hour of time for the presentation. If the policy of your congregation states that every new proposal must first be presented to one of the several standing committees then that, of course, is the route to follow.

The meeting with the church board usually turns out to be the most difficult of all the presentations because this group of officially elected people have to fit this new project into the budget of the congregation. They probably have a half-dozen other proposals all clamoring for attention. In other words, expect resistance from board members who may be championing other causes. This is only natural and, if your project is listed third or fourth, content yourself to know there will have to be a waiting period. However, the pastor usually knows what proposals are brewing and will be able to suggest certain times when your proposal might fit in very well with their planning for the future. Be sure to ask the pastor to decide when the presentation should be made.

If and when the official board decides in favor of the proposal, they still will usually need lead time of say three months, to a year.

It is at this point that it would be wise to begin to organize a health cabinet/committee.

STEP FOUR

FORM A HEALTH CABINET/COMMITTEE

We are convinced that every church which has a parish nurse should have an ongoing health committee or health cabinet which can become true support for the nurse and to which she reports on a monthly basis.

The health cabinet is usually made up of six to a dozen people in the congregation who have some interest in the relationship of religion and health. Health cabinets, if possible, should include a doctor and one or two nurses and perhaps a social worker, a health educator and a school teacher, as well as housewives and business people.

The pastor is an important ex-officio member of the health cabinet and it is hoped that he/she will be present at every meeting. This is of great importance because the parish nurse serves under the pastor's direction and is considered a vital member of the ministerial staff.

The Cabinet will be responsible for:

1. Educating its members about wholistic concepts of health care through regular discussions of recommended books and articles.

2. Assessing the particular kinds of needs which the congregation would like to have the parish nurse address.

3. Working out the financial and legal arrangements. (See the appendix.)

4. Recruiting, interviewing and selecting the parish nurse.

5. Making it possible for the nurse to attend continuing education opportunities, both at home and away, on a regular basis.

6. Keeping the congregation informed of the parish nurse's work through regular items in the church newsletter, as well as through reports of the health cabinet to the official board of the church.

7. Developing opportunities for meetings with neighborhood churches and local hospitals to discuss ways of integrating similar programs.

8. Assisting in planning and executing health fairs, as well as seminars to which the community is invited.

STEP FIVE

LINK UP WITH A LOCAL HOSPITAL (AN OPTION)

In our experimental model of the parish nurse in the Chicago area, we found it very advantageous to have a close tie with a hospital. While it is quite feasible for a church to support a successful parish nurse project on its own, there are some benefits to a hospital relationship you should consider.

Since the role of the parish nurse is new and not well defined, it can be difficult working in a church isolated from peers. The advantage of a relationship with a hospital supplies the need for a parish nurse to have colleague support from other nurses on a regular basis.

Whenever, say, there are two to six churches in the same general area it would be helpful if a hospital, somewhat central to all of them, be chosen as the weekly or semi-weekly meeting place. The hospital might provide allied health professionals to give continuing education for the nurses and facilitate their regular meetings.

It is wise for churches planning a parish nurse project to have, early on, a discussion meeting with people at the local hospital. If there is a department of pastoral care, talk over the idea with the chaplains first. Ideally, this is the department that already relates to the local churches and forward-thinking chaplains quickly grasp the possibilities of the parish nurse concept.

After a discussion with the chaplains, go on to talk with the administrator of the hospital and his/her staff, as well as key members of the board of directors. You may be concerned about selling the parish nurse project to the administrator, but it is often easier than expected. There is a new spirit among hospitals today which lays great emphasis on the relationship of the hospital to the local community. Whereas in the past hospitals were seen as chiefly concerned about people who were sick enough to be put to bed, now hospitals see their task much more wholistically. They are gradually responding to opportunities to teach people how to stay well. Hospitals now see that their future lies in quite different areas than in the past. They really want to be seen as "wellness" institutions, not just sickness institutions.

The degree of hospital involvement is negotiable. When the administrator expresses support for the concept of the parish nurse project, be prepared to offer suggestions for how the hospital might become involved. Here are descriptions of three levels of involvement:

1) The first level would be that the local hospital would provide a meeting room for the small number of parish nurses who would come together for approximately three hours on a weekly or semi-weekly basis.

The main reason for meeting in a hospital rather than taking turns meeting in one of the churches is to develop a relationship with the medical and nursing staff. The hospital would be asked to provide one of their nurse educators as coordinator of this regular seminar group. This educator would listen to the kinds of questions which the parish nurses are raising and then invite other professionals from the staff to share their expertise when it is needed. This provides the kind of back-up so necessary in the early stages of a new development in the profession of nursing.

2) The second level would include all of the things mentioned above plus a close relationship to a hospital's chaplaincy department. In this situation the Chaplain, or one of the several chaplains, might be appointed to be a coordinator with the nurse educator. Needless to say it would be very helpful to have a theologically trained person who could sit in with the parish nurses on a regular basis to raise the many new concerns brought about by an attempt to integrate the physical and spiritual dimensions of illness and health.

If there is no pastoral care department in the hospital then certain community clergy who have been clinically trained in hospital work and counseling might act as coordinators.

3) The third level is when the local hospital actually initiates a parish nurse program in its catchment area. In this case the hospital selects a person to coordinate the project. This person then finds three to six churches and negotiates with them to test out the idea of having nurses on their staffs. If this extensive involvement of the hospital with the church appeals to you, more will be found in chapter four. This describes in some detail the arrangements made with Lutheran General Hospital including financial and educational arrangements.

STEP SIX

SELECT A PARISH NURSE

The pastor of the church and members of the health cabinet will bear the chief responsibility for the selection of the parish nurse. You will need to find a qualified person to screen the candidate's medical qualifications. Perhaps this will be done through your hospital or a physician who has agreed to serve as back-up for the nurse.

There are various sources through which you can recruit your nurse. These include placing a story in your church newsletter, or an advertisement in your local paper and nursing journals. If you are working in conjunction with a local hospital, they can recruit through their channels.

An early question is: Does this nurse have to be a member of the local congregation? Our experience convinces us that it does not matter. We have had some churches where the nurse was, and is, an active member. In some situations the nurse belongs to another church. In other situations Protestant churches have chosen Catholic nurses. In these cases the churches were pleased with their selection.

Among the many things we have learned is the fact that the nurse needs to have a great deal of visibility. Because of the quiet nature of her work people need to reminded of her presence and availability. She should be present in the church every Sunday morning, even participating from time to time in reading scripture at worship services and making special announcements concerning coming events related to the health ministry. She should also sit in on educational programs and enjoy the fellowship hour over refreshments. When she is that visible, it is then easy for members to converse with her. This often leads to people wanting to talk with her further at an appointed time.

The qualifications for a parish nurse are dependent upon the job description (See Appendix) which the health cabinet develops. We have mentioned some of these things before in other connections, but let us restate our belief that all candidates must be registered nurses, preferably with a bacalaureate degree. If your church hopes to serve people who do not have access to a physician, then you will probably need to consider a nurse practitioner.

The nurse you choose will need to be a quietly assertive person. She will have to make herself known in many different ways at least during the early years of this project because the average person will take a while to learn how best to utilize her talents.

At the time of this writing, the nurse's main objective is to help people assume responsibility for their own health and help them grasp new insights concerning the many causes of illness. This entails considerable teaching and forming of support groups. She will have to sell these programs to the people.

A parish nurse must be a sensitive listener so that people will feel comfortable in her presence and know that she cares. In her caring she is picking up on what they are really trying to express. To do this she will, hopefully, have counseling aptitudes. Skills in this area can be improved by attending workshops or training programs.

The nurse you select should also be skilled in recruiting and training volunteers who can be taught to assist her in many different ways including their knowledge of fellow members who are going through difficulties that could bring on illness.

The chief qualification is that she be spiritually mature. In our interviews with many parish nurse candidates we were pleased, but not surprised, to see how many of them could articulate their Christian faith in a manner that was quiet but forceful. We have found that such maturity is essential to developing this unique program in the context of a worshiping and serving congregation. Such a parish nurse will often find herself in a situation where a religious comment or a spoken prayer in the presence of a worried parishioner who has come to her for help is more valuable than any physical ministry. If she has the ability to discuss faith concepts with those who are raising value questions she becomes even more helpful to them.

Nurses engaged in secular work are not usually expected to be able to deal with the spiritual as well as the physical problems of the people who come to them. Parish nurses are encouraged to move into the area of caring simply because we now know that illness always has a dimension which is outside the realm of science. It has been neglected to the detriment of both the patient and the nurse.

We expect our parish nurses to be highly competent medically, but we also hope they are willing to be stretched intellectually through challenging books and discussions which speak to practical theological issues.

We believe that the health of a person is largely determined by the quality of his or *outlook on life*. The central concern of the Christian faith has to do with how people view the nature and the destiny of the human being. We claim to be followers of the Christ.

His outlook on life we highly regard. His world view, his cosmic view, his concept of the kind of relationship that can take place between a human being and one's Creator — all give meaning to our lives. Such an outlook on life is one of the major ingredients of a truly healthy person.

STEP SEVEN

PROVIDE CONTINUING EDUCATION

The nurse your church selects should attend some kind of educational program so that she will be better prepared to meet the demands of her unique position.

The Parish Nurse Program is still so very new that it is not known what to suggest in the way of educational opportunities. Educational programs are beginning to be available in various sections of the country. Most large hospitals offer continuing education courses for nurses and we expect parish nurses to keep up with the medical and scientific side of their profession.

When there are three or more nurses in a certain area, we think it is ideal for them to meet together on a regular basis both to support each other in their unusual responsibilities and to have medical experts sit with them to discuss medical and nursing aspects of their work. Parish nurses must deal with problems which nurses in other specialties may not encounter. These include, especially, the spiritual dimensions of illness. Because of this, it would be well to include a chaplain or knowledgeable parish minister to sit in with the group on a continuing basis.

Knowing that such an arrangement may not be possible, we suggest another idea. For instance, a growing number of hospitals with chaplaincy departments offer courses for local clergy in pastoral care and counseling. Nurses are welcome to participate in these courses. In fact, clergy are always pleased when nurses are also members of their seminars because so many pastoral problems presented have a physical or psychological component. Clergy know that nurses always have something to add to the discussion of a patient's spiritual needs. Nurses are special; they seem to have one foot in medicine and one foot in theology. Because of this, they are natural catalysts who facilitate communication between theology and medicine.

There are also teaching hospitals which offer extended courses in Clinical Pastoral Education on a weekly basis over a period of six to nine months. Nurses fit beautifully into this style of clinical

26

teaching because they then have all the clinical material they need in their own church setting. This type of "CPE" (Clinical Pastoral Education) instruction constantly raises the body and soul issues which are precisely what the nurse in a church setting deals with every day.

The Parish Nurse Resource Center can offer guidance to churches searching for continuing educational opportunities for their parish nurses.

STEP EIGHT

THE PARISH NURSE BEGINS

The first two or three weeks are spent introducing the parish nurse to the congregation and helping them understand what her role will be in the ministry of that church.

On a Sunday, shortly after her arrival, it would be well to arrange a worship service or a special gathering devoted to the theme, "The Role of the Congregation in the Health Ministry of the Church." A sermon by the pastor or/and several brief presentations by church members could then detail the underlying reasons for this new ministry. The parish nurse would then be formally introduced to the people and she would respond with her own statement of her understanding of her ministry.

Such a special service or gathering is essential if this program is to get off to a good start. The people must see it right from the beginning as an integral part of the whole-person ministry of that church.

The following are some of the things which a nurse can do during the first few weeks:

1. Get settled in the room that will be her office. It should be located in a place that is easily accessible, even to wheelchairs. It should, of course, have a telephone. It should offer privacy to those who come to speak with her.

2. Spend considerable time with the pastor and the church staff brainstorming about how this program will be related to the other programs of the church. Staff should have a chance for considerable input for in fact they usually have their finger on the pulse of the congregation.

3. Arrange semi-weekly meetings, during the first month or two, with the Health Cabinet so that they all can become well acquainted with each other and their nurse. During these early weeks the nurse will have many questions to raise.

4. Meet with chairpersons of various standing committees of the church. Only as these church leaders become acquainted with her and learn of her interests and abilities will they be able to use her talents effectively.

5. On several Sundays offer blood pressure checking after and/or between morning services. This provides an excellent way to meet the nurse and the people can decide whether they would like to have further conversations with her.

6. After getting settled the nurse can make herself available to meet with small groups to discuss subjects of their choosing related to the areas of the nurse's competence.

7. Begin to put together a file of the shut-ins and elderly so that she may visit them and make an assessment concerning their needs. She will not become the home health nurse, but she will then be in a position to ascertain whether church volunteers could assist such persons.

8. Survey the congregation to find out where their needs lie. Such a survey will also help her discover what skills are available within the membership and which people might be willing to volunteer their services.

Chapter Four

THE HISTORY OF THE PARISH NURSE PROGRAM

It might be of value to those who would like to start a Parish Nurse program to read a brief outline of the experiences I had in getting the experiment underway in the Chicago area.

We had made a trial run of the idea in Tucson, Arizona at Our Saviour's Lutheran Church which is located across the street from the University of Arizona College of Medicine. For three winters I had been on the faculty of the Medical School in the department of Family and Community Medicine. A few of us had been talking about how we might help a local congregation see that it could play an important role in preventive medicine which means helping people to learn how to stay well.

One of the professional staff members, a former teaching nun, immediately became excited about the potential of such an experiment. Before long, the congregation across the street became interested in putting a Minister of Health on its staff and she was invited to be that person. She set up a wellness clinic in the church. There she presents health educational seminars and does personal health counseling which includes physical examinations. Her work is highly regarded. In a number of ways, I am indebted to her for her pioneering efforts.

I was tremendously impressed with the success of the Tucson venture. When I returned to Chicago from my winter quarter assignment I immediately approached several church-related hospitals in the Chicago area. The idea of a Parish Nurse project was well received. I told the story repeatedly to administrators, chaplains, nurses, physicians and other hospital personnel. Since most of the hospital administrators were open to the idea, I felt we would have no real obstacles to setting up a pilot project.

But I had not counted on conservative hospital board members who, although active in their own churches, could not understand why congregations should get involved in health care. They had never given much thought to the split between the physical and the spiritual in our present health care system. As a result of this resistance some of the hospital administrators wisely decided to put off the project for a while.

One of the hospitals I approached was Lutheran General

Hospital in Park Ridge, Illinois, a suburb northwest of Chicago. This hospital, which has taken its Christian ministry very seriously saw this project falling in line with their many other experimental models of spiritual ministry.

It took about a year and half to get the project under way. We had to decide in which department of the hospital the Parish Nurse Program belonged because it combines several disciplines. For a time we considered placing it under Home Health Care. As we discussed that option we saw such an affiliation would expect our parish nurses to do so much "hands-on" care in homes that there would be little time left to develop the unique model we were striving for in whole person health and wellness care.

In the end it was decided that the parish nurses would become part of the Division of Pastoral Care in close association with the Division of Nursing of the hospital. This has become a most productive association.

The Pastoral Care Departments of most hospitals have a natural affinity with congregations and this one had recently included more and more lay people from congregations —especially nurses — in their regularly scheduled clinical education courses. These courses deal with precisely the areas of greatest interest to parish nurses.

In making the choices concerning which churches to invite to participate in this project, we had to consider that each church would have to find about ten or eleven thousand dollars a year for the salary of a half-time nurse. This limited us to large churches in affluent neighborhoods for the first two or three years. At that point we would be in a better position to know how to work with smaller churches in middle and lower income neighborhoods.

I visited some twenty large churches and told the story of the Parish Nurse Program, first to the pastor of the church and then, if he showed interest, to three or four small groups in that congregation. These groups included evenings of discussion with social ministry committees, nurses groups, health professionals and several members of the official church council. We usually did pretty well until we met with the church's finance committee. Then things bogged down. They had other priorities. Ten thousand dollars a year was more than they cared to risk on such a radical idea. Soon I learned that churches do not have an item in their budget for "risk taking."

After several months of almost nightly conversations with groups in the twenty churches I felt that we had several churches willing to join in this venture. But gradually it become clear as we neared the signing ceremony that there was actually only one congregation willing or able to take on the entire financial responsibility. The project almost ended at that point.

Lutheran General Hospital then came to our aid. They agreed to offer churches a three year contract whereby the hospital, during the first year, would pay three-fourths of the nurse's salary, one-half the second year and one-fourth the third year, with the congregation picking up the entire cost of the following years.

Even with this encouragement the finance committee of most of the churches demurred for the present. We finally found six congregations willing to take on this responsibility over a three year period. Two of these churches were Roman Catholic and four were Protestant. They ranged in distance from the hospital from four blocks to thirty miles.

Each congregation was asked to organize a Health Cabinet made up of eight to a dozen members who were interested in the area of health, wholeness and the spiritual dimensions of life. At this stage their main responsibility was to find the right nurse for this particular church. This Cabinet was also to serve as the support group for this new nurse. Although she would report directly to the pastor in her daily work, this group of people could work closely with her as she began a type of ministry which this congregation had never before experienced.

We advertised for nurse candidates through the usual channels. Within two weeks we had almost thirty candidates. Nurses from as far away as Denver applied, hoping we would have picked a congregation in their area of the country. Of the thirty applicants who were screened and interviewed we were surprised to find fifteen or twenty who fulfilled all our requirements. This convinced us that throughout the country there are thousands of nurses who are looking for opportunities to use their many talents in special forms of Christian ministry.

The final selection of the nurse was made by the congregation. The hospital's nursing department did the screening for the medical and technical requirements. The pastoral care department sought to determine the nurse's potential for bringing the medical and the spiritual dimensions together.

A few months before the nurses began their work, we organized a faculty to think through the kind of continuing education program might best fit the needs of this unusual kind of ministry for nurses. The faculty consisted of physicians, nurses and chaplains from the hospital's staff. We were in immediate agreement that we did not want to superimpose a curriculum on this first group of nurses, all of whom had a rich background of experience. Since their role, as we were now defining it, had yet to be tested, we could not pretend to anticipate their needs. Their course of instruction would have to be an evolving process with the nurses influencing its creation. Consequently our structure was kept flexible from the outset.

The nurses met each week for four or more hours beginning each Wednesday morning by participating in the regular chapel service with the hospital chaplains. This was always followed by a period of fellowship at the coffee time when chaplains and nurses could get acquainted — there being some twenty five chaplains at Lutheran General.

When the nurses met in their classroom we usually began by asking each nurse to tell us what kinds of experiences she had during the previous week. It took from an hour to an hour-and-a-half for these six nurses to describe their experiences. The discussion and the emotions shared as each nurse recounted the happenings in which she was involved left all of us exhausted by the end of the class hour. But we were also exhilarated by hearing how these nurses were touching the lives of people in ways that had never before happened in those congregations. Growing out of these provocative discussions a flexible curriculum gradually emerged.

The first three months of the nurse's work in the congregations was mostly a time to introduce whole-person health care concepts. This was done in many different ways. One of the best ways was through regular blood pressure testing on Sunday mornings. Large numbers of people responded, many of them asking to have personal conversations with the nurse at another time. Such contact led naturally to people seeing the nurse as a personal health counselor.

The nurse then arranged discussion groups and seminars where either she presented the material or she brought in experts from the outside to speak. The nurse was always present so that members could speak with her later about specific matters generated by the presentations.

In congregations where the nurse got off to a slower start than in others we learned that it was often due to inadequate preparation of the key members of the church. We who have worked with the project for many months just assume that after one long meeting with leading church members the whole idea of the project will be understood. What we have to remember is that for many people the idea of health care and wellness being brought into the church is a radical idea. They actually have never heard that there is a close working relationship between the body and the soul. Even when they do begin to grasp the idea they have to have it explained to them over and over again before they can begin to explain it to other members of the church.

Lay church leaders need to be involved early on in making the major decisions concerning the employment of a nurse on their staff. If the decision is made only by the pastor it usually will not work. The pastor, of course, has to be solidly in back of it, but it is just as important for the lay people to be for it. The goal is for the active church members to feel that they own the project. This can happen only when they are participants in the early decision making process.

Chapter Five

ONE NURSE'S EXPERIENCE — THE FIRST YEAR

"Trinity Church" (not the actual name) is a large 1,600 member church in a Chicago suburb. There are three full-time ministers. In March of 1985, the Church council agreed to be one of the pilot churches for the Parish Nurse Program. The Health Cabinet was formed immediately as a sub-committee of the Christian Education board of the congregation. It consisted of three doctors, a school nurse, two other nurses, a hospital administrator, a home-maker, a university professor and a businessman. Its very first task was to select a nurse to serve on the staff of their church. Looking back, it is now felt that the health cabinet should have had more time to develop their understanding of the goals and objectives of this unique position. They were not at all clear on what the expectations should be of this new parish nurse. This would have put them in a better position to interview candidates.

Several candidates for the position were screened by Lutheran General Hospital Nursing and Pastoral Care staff. Not one of the candidates was a member of this church. A nurse who was a member of this church, (whom we shall call Carol — not her name), did not apply because she considered the job description much too broad. Also she felt there was more emphasis on the spiritual aspect than she believed she was capable of handling.

It was during the health cabinet's second meeting that they interviewed nurses for the position. The interviews were hurried, in group form and poorly done. Since the cabinet was not clear what it wanted in a nurse their questions were unrelated and without substance.

In the end it was decided that none of the nurses would fit the needs of this particular church although they were women of exceptional ability. To Carol's surprise the health cabinet unanimously decided that she should become their parish nurse. She accepted largely because she wanted to see the project succeed.

Carol has a BSN and Master's credits in adult education. She has worked for two years as a school nurse, twelve years as a pediatrics nurse and ten years in a women's clinic where she was involved in health education.

With the exception of seven years she has lived in the area all her life and has attended Trinity since she was two years old. As a result she has many positive connections with the medical community. The time-consuming task of building the initial relationships was behind her. Doctors respected her because they knew she was a nurse first. People at Trinity had had years to size her up. They knew her to be very honest about her own life. This has given many people the courage to confide in her.

Carol began her work in May. She believes it is a good time of the year to start because it takes about three months to gear up for any kind of program. Since the church slows down it's pace in the summer, she was at liberty to prepare for Fall activities.

The health cabinet was scheduled to meet once a month with Carol. Rather than being a board to which she merely reported, Carol saw the wisdom of encouraging all of the members to see themselves as partners in this project. This meant that they themselves would participate in many of the specially planned activities. Programs are not presented by just the parish nurse. They are presented by the "Health Cabinet and the Parish Nurse." This partnership brought out hidden talents among the health cabinet members. "They were not going to allow for shoddy programming. They took their responsibilities seriously," were Carol's comments.

When Carol came on staff considerable attention was given to her new position through the weekly newsletter and the church bulletin. The weekly newsletter became a major vehicle for communication. Carol includes something in it every week to keep the congregation current on the role of a nurse in the church.

Her first major project was to discover the needs of the people who made up her 1,600 member congregation. Carol designed a health survey. This was distributed at all three Sunday services. The pastor took about five minutes during each service to explain the purpose of this survey and gave people ample time to fill it out. It was collected in the offering plate that day. Because time was provided during the service, there was an unusually good response. The health cabinet studied the results of the survey and then developed programs which fit the needs of the congregation.

Carol spent the entire summer laying her groundwork. She chose to have an office that was away from the church offices to ensure confidentiality, but still accessible to the elderly. Since there was no budget outside of her salary all her equipment was donated.

She spent weeks developing a health file cabinet. This was

topical. She went to health agencies getting information about special health-related issues. She wrote letters to societies that were located far away asking them to send her information.

She visited countless agencies in the community to let them know who she was and to learn more about them: home health agencies, hospitals, senior citizen's centers and mental health nurses were among her targets. She never had trouble getting appointments — even with hospital administrators. She thinks they were curious about what a Parish Nurse was. Home health agencies were grateful to learn that she was not planning to duplicate their services. Through those visits not only did she promote her role, but she also could decide whether or not a particular agency was a good referral.

During the summer the only health education she did was for vacation Bible school — she could not resist. She offered four topics to the teachers and their classes — they could choose to attend two. The topics were: (1) "How to brush your teeth." For this she had gotten small tubes of toothpaste from local dentists to give each child. (2) Nutrition" (3) "Seat Belts," and (4) "The Big, Bad Cigarette," complete with coloring books.

In September the Health Cabinet and Carol began implementing their monthly health education course. Each of these met at Forum from 11:00 - 12:00 on Sunday morning. Advertisements for events were placed in the church newsletter and bulletin as well. The kick-off was a course about how the stress of the mind causes disease. It was taught by a medical doctor who is a professor at the University of Illinois School of Medicine. He is a member of the church.

September also saw the start-up of a highly successful weight loss group which met weekly and blood pressure testing between Sunday services. Carol got the use of a large bulletin board on which she posts timely articles and events.

In September Carol became highly visible, but there were still few people knocking on her door for personal health counseling. The blood pressure testing opened the door for some people to feel comfortable talking with her about other problems, but she needed more. If anything was to happen she would have to initiate it.

Every week she went through the bulletin and got the names of those ill or hospitalized. She visited the people in the hospital. She called the spouse at home and asked how they were doing and if there was anything she could do. If a husband had to go to a nursing home she would go with the wife to the three or four homes suggested by the hospital social worker. She would make sure that the questions were asked and answered to the wife's satisfaction.

Carol called up the former church organist, a woman in her 80's. She asked her for a list of shut-ins that might benefit from a visit. The organist was glad to comply and soon sent a list of almost one hundred people. Overwhelmed, but willing, Carol called each name on the list and visited each person that desired it.

Through visits such as these she became convinced of the need for a Parish Nurse to have training in general physical assessment (something all nurses do not have). Time and time again, the nurse is called upon to assess the general health of a person in order to connect them to medical help. Carol feels training in public health nursing is also essential so that when she goes into a home she knows what to observe about the surroundings and the people, what to say, what not to say, and to assess the home situation as it applies to mental and physical health.

Over time other people filtered into the Parish Nurse's office on their own — even adolescents. Typically people would come in with one complaint, like a headache. As they talked, more problems were uncovered. One teenager came to Carol because of being overweight. It was not long before Carol learned that there was considerable family stress. She invited the parents to come in, which they did and soon was able to link them up with a family counselor.

Carol was cautious about starting support groups. She questioned her qualifications for such a venture. To date, there is the weight support group and an arthritis group which meets monthly and brings in a speaker each time.

Organizing volunteers was a project which Carol waited until January to tackle. Recognizing that she had no training in working with volunteers she went to the local hospital and a few other agencies and talked with the directors of volunteers. From them she essentially took a tailor-made course in "volunteers." She set up her project by drafting the former church secretary to be the coordinator because she had the advantage of knowing virtually everyone at Trinity. They recruited fifty women for the "We Care" committee. These women are now organized to provide emergency meals, transportation, babysitting and to visit the large number of shut-ins from the membership.

To augment her work still further she supervised two nursing students from the nearby college. One of their projects was to put on a mini-health fair in January on a Sunday morning. The congregation was delighted. As usual there was blood pressure testing. A local optometrist did glaucoma and vision testing. A hospital employee came and measured pulmonary functioning (lung capacity). The Red Cross gave ongoing CPR demonstrations.

Carol has been the Parish Nurse at Trinity Church for one year now. She usually puts in a 30-hour work, although she is only paid for 20 hours. She derives much satisfaction from her job because she can use all her talents. She also loves working with the members of Trinity and finds the "small" accomplishments very rewarding.

In addition to what is incorporated into this writing she cautions prospective Parish Nurses about a few things: "The job description is broad. Don't try to do everything right away. It will take at least three months just to lay the groundwork — much longer if you are new to the community."

"A Parish Nurse must be able to work independently. Despite approval by the congregation and staff for the nurse, she is isolated. Ministers are already very busy with their own responsibilities. Don't expect strokes from the staff. The rewards will come from the people with whom you work."

Chapter Six

THEOLOGICAL REFLECTIONS ON JESUS' MINISTRY
by Jill Westberg McNamara

One cannot think of healing or be a part of healing without reflection upon the figure of Him who is the Author and Finisher of our healing as well as our faith. Krister Stendahl has said, "God's agenda is the mending of creation." Mending is an expression for God's total love toward suffering humanity, of which healing is an aspect. We can say that the healing light of Jesus Christ has always been in the world, as an indication of life-giving and sustaining concern.

He promised that we would do greater works than He and it is clear that he demands no slavish repetition, but rather a lively and creative response to his spirit. Yet, there can be no argument that the approach to the healing task, both in spirit and in practice, must be drawn from the Healing Christ. The rhythm of preaching, teaching and healing runs all the way through Christ's ministry. Those who came to Him reflected that rhythm, for they came "to listen to Him and to be healed of their disease." Again, and again the phrase that is found in the scriptures says, "and He healed every kind of disease and infirmity." Jesus accepted the human condition, focused on core realities and dealt with them. All of life is interrrelated and plays on health. An individual human being is an interactive totality of body, mind and soul, emotion and will. Health in human beings in community is affected by almost every condition and influence that runs through life.

The New Testament makes it clear that Jesus' ministry stressed healing the whole person. Almost one-fifth of the Gospels is devoted to his healings and discussions that resulted from them. (Kelsey, *Healing and Christianity*, p.54.)

In the Hebrew culture of Jesus, the body and spirit were not divorced. Jesus viewed the individual as an essential unity and because of this he was able to envision more clearly than those who had preceded him the essential wholeness of life. He was always concerned about healing a person whose body showed signs of illness, but he rarely ended at that point. He paid close attention to other manifestations of illness in the person's life.

Jesus dealt with relationships within the person, between the

41

person and God, between the person and neighbor and between the person and the world. These relationships gave a necessary perspective to the picture and allowed healing to be approached in a wholistic way.

Experiences of relationship and intimacy also give evidence that human life is whole and not fragmented. Energy we experience after settling a dispute is more than emotional; the pleasure of sexual intimacy is more than physical; the sharing of prayer and belief in a community faith is more than spiritual. Human relationships involve the whole of ourselves. We are totally involved, whether we are hearing of a painful betrayal or sharing an affirmative hug. Relationship is wholistic, and, therefore, a dimension of health.

Experiences of belief and faith, commonly considered to be spiritual or mental, actually pervade all of human experience. The person who lives with hope interprets life differently and therefore, acts and feels differently. There is more physical energy, more mental clarity, more freedom in relationships when we live with a hope-full faith. Conversely, when our outlook on life is based in guilt, retribution and fear, there is more fear-related adrenaline released, more stomach acid flowing, more defensive muscle tension. Faith and health are interrelated not only in times of dramatic healing, but they are inseparable every day of our "healthy" lives!

Experiences which we consider to be emotional also involve our whole selves. The relief that often follows crying is more than emotional; we take a deep breath, clear our thoughts and get on with our lives, a little more whole than before. Laughter often functions in the same way, renewing our perspective and liberating us physically. Experts in "mental health" are discovering what we've experienced for years: that anxiety, depression and other problems involve the whole person including their relationships, their faith, their physical state and even their eating habits.

Mark 2: 1-12 illustrates how Jesus' healings were not confined to either the physical or the spiritual realm. In the first verses, when a paralytic was brought to Jesus, he said simply, "Son, your sins are forgiven." In doing so he went beyond the paralytic's external ills to touch the deeper causes of the paralysis. The man took up his pallet and walked because Jesus understood that the body and spirit are a unity.

From the scriptures we know that Jesus sent his disciples out to continue his ministry. He told them to preach the kingdom of God and heal the sick. It can be assumed from the healing that Jesus modeled that he intended healing of the *whole* person. The

Book of Acts records how well the early church carried out this commission, caring for whole persons and not just souls or bodies. They were inspired by a sense of wholeness in their mission to the world. They believed that the new quality of life which Christ came to impart, was to extend to the whole of man's being, body, soul, and spirit. Thus from the outset the ministry of healing was considered to be an integral a part of the Church's work as the ministry of Word or Sacrament with which it is fundamentally linked." (Garlick, *Man's Search for Health,* p.184.)

Health as Enabler

The word which most aptly describes health is "enabler." Our health enables us to participate in the salvatory process: to respond to the lure of God, to act on the possibilities which are open to us which lead toward our fulfillment. Health, to some degree, is necessary in order for people to venture and participate in creation. Health is vital because it enables the saving process of human life which brings meaning to health. Salvation gives people a much higher ideal than freedom from suffering or a perfectly adjusted self.

When health is viewed as an enabler, the picture we conjure up in our minds of a healthy person is transformed. We all know people who, despite physical handicaps, lead very healthy lives. By the same token we know people who have everything going for them, but are going no place with it. People who do not take advantage of their health are inhibiting their involvement in the process of living and creation. We also know people who have reached a state of health through illness. The illness enabled them to wrestle with their faith and reach a deeper sense of wholeness in spite of a broken physical body.

From a theological perspective healing is a part of the entire process of living. If health is an enabler then it is an element that can stand to be encouraged no matter what the situation. Also, health is an ongoing process; it is not a state that is reached because there are not symptoms of disease. With this in mind it seems apparent that healing is an activity that is not reserved strictly for the sick. "Healthy" people need care too. Healing needs to be an everyday occurrence.

Chapter Seven

CONGREGATIONAL HEALTH AND HEALTH CABINETS

Since 1970, a number of us have been actively developing Wholistic Health Centers which are family practice doctors' offices located in churches as part of the ministry of these congregations. In each Center, there is an interdisciplinary team consisting of a physician, a pastoral counselor, and a nurse. The patient is seen as an equal member of that healing team, and together, the four of them work in whatever ways are appropriate to promote the physical, mental, and spiritual health of that individual and his/her family.

I have long been bothered by the fact that many of the illnesses doctors see in the final stages could have been prevented if these people had been taught how to change their style of life and their outlook on life. I began to wonder if health education courses in parish churches might be one way to get to people in the earlier stages of illness, when the illness might be reversible. I am convinced that a large percentage of Americans are kept well by their relationship to their communities of faith.

I see Christian congregations as contributing much in the area of preventive medicine. As a member of the faculty of the Department of Preventive Medicine and Community Health of the University of Illinois, College of Medicine at Chicago, we decided to test out this thesis. We have now established a number of family doctors' offices in churches in low-, middle-, and upper-income areas. Professionals in the health field who have examined these Centers tend to agree with Dr. Richard H. Lange in his article appearing in the *New York State Journal of Medicine* (May, 1980):

"A healthy and wholesome application of these (wholistic) concepts is found at the Hinsdale Wholistic Health Center in Illinois, founded by Granger Westberg. The Hinsdale experiment has spawned other successful wholistic centers stressing health care for the total organism. The distinguishing factor of these centers is the practice of scientific medicine with all patients receiving a full medical work-up to uncover any organic diseases. In addition, health education and preventive medicine are emphasized since wholistic doctrine implies individual responsibility and activated patients.

45

. . . These preventive measures and common sense approaches can be an effective complement to today's highly technologic and highly specialized medicine and should be welcomed as old friends. They may need fresh introduction to some of our more technologic and narrowly focused colleagues, but they are nevertheless part of the tradition of medicine."

We have now demonstrated that many churches can have doctors' offices within their own buildings, closely integrated with ministries to their community. But most churches will never be able to have such Centers on their premises due to space and financial requirements. What alternatives can we suggest for congregations to engage in active health care concerns without having a complete doctor's office in their building? My daughter, Jill, has worked with scores of churches developing Health Cabinets, a viable alternative, which she describes in the following way.

Health Cabinets in Churches

Many congregations have asked us, "What can we do for our congregation? We don't have the space or the money or the energy to start a Wholistic Health Center, but we want to do something now about the health of our congregation; we don't want to wait until we have the resources to start a full-blown Center."

The church which I (Jill) attended was one of the churches that asked this question. It is a relatively new church, and one of its premises is that it should be a therapeutic community. We've carried this out fairly well, and it is evident that people in the community minister to one another. For example, we have what is called a "pre-liturgy." Before the actual worship service begins, we have a time set aside when, as a community, we discuss what's going on. These discussions can range anywhere from the typical church announcements saying that there will be a potluck on Wednesday night and please bring a covered dish, to a discussion on the social issues of the day and what we intend to do about them. It can also be a time when we share concerns and joys of the community within the context of intercessory prayers and social action. For example, a woman might stand up and say, "Sue will be coming home from the hospital today. We need to organize some meals for the family because they have too much on their minds to have to worry about cooking. If you're interested and able to help out, please meet me in this corner of the church when the service is over." Pre-liturgy is also a time when we can share with others when we're taking on new ventures. We can let them know what

46

this entails and ask for their support and prayers.

So, here is a church that is dedicated to the concept of the healing ministry, and we're carrying it out in many ways. Still, we wanted to do more in terms of educational programs, raising people's consciousness about the close relationship between health and faith and influencing people's whole approach to life. We believe that this has a great deal to do with our health and unhealth, and we believe that the church is a good place to do this. We felt it was essential that we develop a special Health Cabinet that would be devoted to ministering to the health of the church's life in all its dimensions, not just special events or crisis care.

The healing ministry is central to Christianity. Most churches are very good in crisis care. If someone becomes very sick in the congregation, people rally around to support that individual, to bring meals, help clean the house, take care of the children, or do whatever they can to help. This is all very good, but the question is, "Why do we wait until matters have reached the crisis stage? Why can't we help people when they are in the early stages of illness? Are there things we can do of a preventive nature, and by being supportive of them, could we help to reverse illness before it reaches crisis proportions?"

The other area in which the church functions well is education. There are many courses taught in churches to people of all ages on health-related subjects: Creative Management of Stress is popular; CPR training and Grief and Loss are common subjects of inquiry. Far too often though, these education programs are attended by those people who are already interested in health-related matters. They are not reaching out to everybody — just to a selected few. As I see it, the churches are doing a lot in terms of the healing ministry, but there is so much more that could be done. We're limiting ourselves.

The churches have a great advantage as a healing institution. For instance, it is one of the few institutions in our society that welcomes all ages. It welcomes families, and families are the main health support system of the individual. To have an institution that supports our support system is tremendous. We come to churches together as a family. In other areas of our society, the children go off to school, and the parents go off to work; or the mother to her tennis lesson, the father to the golf course, and the children to Little League. Hopefully, the one place where we can come together as a family is when we go to church.

The church influences our lifestyle. It is one of the few places where it is acceptable to talk about our values. We can look at our values and at our lifestyles and see whether they conflict or whether they are actually in harmony with each other.

The church is a place where we are accepted both in sickness and in health. We don't need a pain for a ticket of admission, and we're still o.k. if we do get sick. One real advantage that I see in this is that when we do become sick, we're surrounded by people who have known us in health. They know our strengths even though they are now hidden because we're so consumed by illness. They can call forth these strengths which help us overcome our illness.

The Christian perspective on health is unique. In our society, the traditional approach is disease-oriented. Health is defined as the absence of disease. This negative approach stresses fear as the motivation for moving toward health. Even preventive medicine is often performed out of a sense of fear. We get our immunizations so that we won't get that dread disease. The whole time we are preventing illness, we are looking over our shoulder at this fearful object — disease. In this traditional approach, health is seen as an end in itself. There is not much beyond that. In the Christian perspective, health is seen as an on-going process. Health is not an end in itself. Health instead is an enabler. It enables us to serve and to love others. Health is seen in the context of purpose. It is the liberator. And so, with this Christian perspective, we have the possibility and the reality of health promotion and not just disease prevention.

The model that we finally chose for our congregation was that of the "Health Cabinet." We chose this name because most homes have a medicine cabinet, and so why shouldn't the church have a health cabinet? The Health Cabinet is a tool, a way of involving the congregation in a healing ministry to each other. It is based on the wholistic philosophy which understands that the individual is an integrated whole — body, mind, and spirit — and each dimension is inextricably bound up with the whole. We can't be satisfied with looking only at a person's spirit or only at the physical side because each dimension is so bound up with the others that in touching one dimension, we're bound to affect the whole person and not just the part we directly touch.

The individual also needs to be seen in the context of the community — in this case, in the context of their family and the church community. We are all related to each other. It is from community that we derive our support and our encouragement, and this frees us to move toward the health of our whole person.

This Health Cabinet is made up of a group of volunteers who are concerned about health and who are committed to seeing that the healing ministry in our church is carried out. The Health Cabinet assists individuals and families to become more responsible for maintaining and improving their own health and that of their community. The Cabinet is not involved in diagnosis and treatment. This is the domain of the person's family physician. The Health Cabinet seeks to act as a strong influence in the life of the congregation to insure that the stewardship of health is expressed in worship, education, networks of support, and recreation.

The Health Cabinet works in three main areas. The first is through sponsoring health-related changes or activities through already existing "structures" such as the worship, Sunday School classes, youth groups, whatever. For instance, a member of the Health Cabinet might offer to teach a session in various Sunday School classes for different ages on "Your Faith and Your Health." Or, at a social event that is scheduled by another organization, they might encourage them to have people bring to the potluck healthy-type foods to let people know that they can eat food that is healthy, and it still tastes good. Another alternative is to encourage the Book Club to include books on health-related subjects.

A second front in which the Health Cabinet involves itself is the sponsorship of programs or activities without going through these already existing structures. For instance, if there is a real interest in the church in a particular area of health, they bring in outside speakers and make this a special event. The Health Cabinet also might put on a "Health Fair" that devotes a particular Sunday to the healing ministry. This includes the worship service as well as activities after the service — a sermon on the healing elements of faith, contemporary readings on how our faith is actually related to health, Biblical readings which refer to the healings of Jesus. After the service, there are activities that involve people in various stress testing exercises. Activities are promoted that really involve people and get them to understand what is meant by wellness. These activities are followed by a potluck lunch of healthy foods which are described by the ones who brought them. Recipes are then shared.

The third area of activity is the one I consider most important and essential if the Health Cabinet is to strongly influence the health of the church. In this third front, the Health Cabinet looks at the overall health and unhealth in the life of the whole congregation. They work at ways in which to support the health and turn the unhealth around. We seek to develop a network of resources within the community, the resources being the people and what they have to offer just in being themselves; a supportive network.

Each one of us has been through some painful experiences in our lives and have made it through. Even though we might not be professionals, we've learned a lot through these experiences, and we have something to share with other people. And so, when someone is going through a divorce, or an illness, or is having to deal with peer pressure, we can refer them to someone who can walk with them through these areas. If nothing else, they offer a listening and sympathetic ear.

In conclusion, the Health Cabinet looks at ways in which we can become more sensitive to the needs of others, and it looks at ways in which we can encourage people to be more open with each other, to be more sharing, more of a healing community to each other. This is truly a major goal of the Christian congregation.

Chapter Eight

WHOLE PERSON AND WHOLE EARTH
by Carl E. Braaten

Introductory note: The Parish Nurse program has its primary roots in the history and theology of our Judeo-Christian experience through the centuries.

We are, therefore, including a provocative article by an eminent Christian theologian, Professor Carl E. Braaten. It may be somewhat difficult reading. It is quite a radical expression of why the Christian church ought to take health and preventive medicine more seriously. If you enjoy being challenged to wrestle with unusual ideas, please take the time to read this article at least twice. You won't be sorry you did. (Professor Braaten gave his personal permission to include this portion of an article which appeared in *Lutheran Women* May, 1986.)

THE MEEK SHALL INHERIT THE EARTH

Humanity and earth exist together in a mutually dependent relationship. A person cannot be whole without a whole earth. When the earth becomes sick, people become sick. A human being is part of the earth, and the earth is part of human being.

My theme here is more precisely the human body and the food of the earth. Absolutely no wisdom on this subject can be found in the great biblical and systematic theologies of recent times, in spite of a lot of talk about Luther's "whole man." Christian theology has dealt mostly with the salvation drama — creation and fall, sin and guilt, cross and resurrection, the church and the last things. The question of the health of the body and of the earth has rarely been posed. But in the biblical vision salvation is no partial process that concerns merely a part of the totality of reality, the part called the "soul." The biblical vision is all-embracing, the earth goes together with heaven and the body goes together with the soul. Salvation includes health and healing.

Today humanity is faced with the question of its own survival on the earth. The term "eco-crisis" has been coined to dramatize this ecological question. Humans are placing a great strain on the earth, and the earth is in pain. With technology as their club, human beings have been beating the earth to death as though it were something to be hated. The earth will tolerate only so much of our human nonsense; after that a process called "dieback" may be triggered. The human species may die back to the point where it barely survives at all.

51

DUST THOU ART, AND UNTO DUST SHALT THOU RETURN

The biblical basis for stressing our human continuity with the good earth around us is expressed classically in Genesis 3:19: "In the sweat of thy face shalt thou eat bread, till thou return unto the ground; for out of it wast thou taken; for dust thou art, and unto dust shalt thou return." The Christian doctrine of creation has tended to neglect the earthly medium of the creation of homo sapiens. Humanity is not external to the earth, but one of its vital forms. The earthly environment gives the human being physical, mental and spiritual food. There is no direct, unmediated relation between God and humanity in the history of creation and redemption. The earth is always there as a third partner — a creative medium; hence the expression "mother earth." Adama is the Hebrew name for earth, whose first son is Adam, the man. The earth is a womb, home and grave for Adam.

When we moderns destroy the balance of nature, not only are soil, plants and animals affected, but the human body also pays a price. The earth lashes back, and the harmony between earth and humanity is destroyed.

Would we continue to plunder our environment if we saw ourselves as bodies in natural continuity with the earth. "For no one ever hated his own body: on the contrary, he provides and cares for it" (Ephesians 5:29). If the body is seen as the very stuff of the earth, then such a thing as soil erosion will not be viewed with indifference, but as a serious disease of the body. Similarly, the spreading of the human species on the earth beyond the capacity of this small planet to provide each member a full measure of healthful food will be regarded as a terminal illness, as fatal as a cancer growing in the body. An infinitely expanding GNP can be seen as another form of cancer in the whole body of humanity and earth.

What we must hope for is a new attitude to the physical world, consisting of a profound respect for the delicate connections between all creatures and a mystical harmony with the earth as the source and ground of our bodily life. Albert Schweitzer's philosophy of reverence for life must be commended in spite of the fact that it was nourished by Eastern mysticism rather than by Christianity. Ralph Waldo Emerson and Henry David Thoreau were also exponents of an earth mysticism. Emerson wrote: "The greatest delight which the fields and woods minister is the suggestion of an occult relation between Man and vegetable."

Western philosophy has inherited a prejudice against nature. It has been predominantly a philosophy of ideas (Plato) or of consciousness (Descartes) and more recently of existence (Heidegger) or of language (Wittgenstein), but the bodily basis of thought is not reflected in any of these great systems.

In marked contrast, the exclusion of body, food and earth would be unthinkable in Eastern philosophy. My investigations have not reached a point where I can explain why Christianity has retained so little of the "somatic" in its spirituality and theology. It has excelled in its stress on individuality and personality, forgetting that it is the body that individuates the personality. Where would I be without my body? The I-Thou relationship is a pure abstraction without the flesh and blood that bump against each other.

Christianity veered into spiritualism as it accommodated to the Greek world. At the same time it mishandled its Jewish sources. It is hard to deny that dominant trends in Christianity have simultaneously nourished supernatural and antinatural attitudes, driving humanity into an egoistic subjectivism, and reducing nature to a mechanism subject to humanity's brutal will.

The body — soul dichotomy reflects itself in a split between man and nature, between the subjective spirit of humanity and objective world.

The Israel of the Old Testament tended to split the world into two realms, opting for the God of history against the God of nature. The struggle between Baal and Yahweh was a struggle between the God of fertility and God of history. What Israel achieved was to make the God of fertility subject to Yahweh, the Lord of history, so that she was liberated from the worship of earth, from cultic participation in the rituals of earth's renewal. But this liberation did not mean that in entering history, she abandoned nature. Israel did not expel the mysteries of fertility, did not sever its connection with the earth. The promises she lived from include hope for a good land flowing with milk and honey.

The rectification of an unbalanced attitude toward the earth in Christian spirituality will require us to be more radical in our approach to the Old Testament.

We will have to look at the creation hymns and at the hymns of judgment in Psalm 104 for example, the poet depicts the world —vegetable, animal and human — as God's creation. God's breath is the life principle of all things. The hymns of judgment arise in face of the evil deeds of mankind. People damage and destroy the creation of God, including themselves. They do not

53

care for the earth, so the earth mourns and languishes by the violence of people (Hosea 4:3). Heaven and earth witness against them; they have the peoples' oaths of allegiance to the Creator, but have suffered the full force of their violence. If we read the Old Testament with eyes renewed by ecological sensitivity, we will see things to which we were blind before. Israel's vision of humanity and its earthly environment can inspire in us a new wisdom of the beauty of the earth made whole, a vision in which union with God includes humanity's commonality with the whole creation.

WE ARE WHAT WE EAT

Nothing more exemplifies our interconnection with the earth than the food we eat. We are what we eat. On the surface, this saying smacks of materialistic reductionism. In this instance, I am adopting the slogan without accepting the materialistic component in Christian spirituality. Both the doctrine of creation and the incarnation make the matter of the earth the medium of the creative Word and Spirit.

Earthly food becomes human life. More simply, by eating from the earth, we live. I am convinced that what we eat provides us with one key to the symbol system in the Bible and Christian faith. In the Bible we do not meet a metaphysics of food such as we find in Oriental philosophy, but we do find a symbolism of food, the residue of which any Christian can recognize in its most concentrated form as the sacrament of eating and drinking.

In early Christian spirituality, eating and drinking were in themselves religious acts. A simple prayer was offered before and after the meal. Family, food and religion were all brought together in the same time and space. Compare that to the secular style in America today. People rush in from the streets, do not compose themselves through any ritual, gulp down some "instant" foods and disperse again as nervous as when they arrived. The religious meaning of eating and drinking has vanished.

In some way — sometimes characterized as paradoxical, sometimes mystical — the presence of God is associated with eating and drinking bread and wine; in some way, the grace of God is communicated through natural food and drink. In Protestantism there has been a progressive tendency to desacralize religion, with the result that eating and drinking also become progressively secularized activities, without ritual, symbolism and sacral meaning.

One of the central religious symbols of the Bible is bread. We pray in the Lord's Prayer. "Give us this day our daily bread." Bread and faith are intertwined in the Bible. If this connection is lost to us, perhaps we can better understand if we say that bread and peace (another biblical symbol) are necessarily linked together in the modern world. We have either bread and peace or hunger and war.

The revolutionary struggle boils down to each human being wanting to get his hand firmly planted on the bread knife. But now, this most precious symbol of life — the very staff of life —has become so devitalized, literally devitaminized, that it loses it's value as food, and therefore also as the symbol of real life.

PHYSICIAN, HEAL THYSELF

All of the great world religions except Christianity emphasize the connection between the divine order of the universe and the dietary principles of the good life. Diet is an essential part of Judaism, Islam and Hinduism. Christianity hails the divorce of religion and diet as an advance into the land of freedom. It would be ludicrous to call for a return to the dietary laws of the Old Testament, but another course is open to us. That is to start a new movement of freedom from bondage to the principles that make ours a sick nation, make a people sick in mind and body.

The chief dynamics of American society cause illness and bad health. The modern practice of medicine is almost entirely symptomatic; it treats symptoms, relieves pain, but neglects the whole person and the conditions of living that excellent health presupposes.

Americans are not healthier than they used to be. The standard of living has been rising since World War II, but the quality of life has been declining. The growth of technology has given us false trust that things are getting better. To be sure, technology has given us new tecniques in sanitation, antiseptics and surgery. And, indeed, many conspicuous diseases have been conquered — diphtheria, polio, tuberculosis. But the degenerative diseases have been quietly galloping into epidemic proportions.

Millions of American suffer from heart disease; they speak of their high blood pressure, arteriosclerosis, of angina. Millions suffer from diabetes or hypoglycemia, both connected with the fact after World War II the consumption of sugar in America rose dramatically. Two disorders directly linked to nutrition are constipation and insomnia.

The concept of the whole person within the whole context of life is blatantly disregarded.

A culture can hardly be called a culture when it rears its youth in almost total ignorance about the fundamental arts of life: farming, cooking, eating, working, playing, exercising, meditating, fasting, praying and making love.

WHAT MUST WE DO TO BE SAVED?

My judgments have been short and snappy. They are intended, however, to provoke us to more reading and reflection. If they can be supported, and I think they can, then they roll themselves into this one question: what must we do to be saved?

I want to emphasize that Christianity ought to reclaim its message of healing. The Christian message is the healing of the whole person, or it is a false religion.

The Appendix

ABOUT THIS APPENDIX

During the start-up years of our program at Lutheran General Hospital we were pleased to have a number of people who had heard about the program come to visit us.

Before we knew it there were several programs under way. Each one was unique in its own way and yet we had the basic principles in common. I thought it would be helpful to our readers to catch something of the flavor of several of these programs. The best way to do this is to include in this appendix some of the actual writings of some of these programs.

As you will see, no two programs are exactly alike. Each program indicates a good deal of creative dreaming and planning. There might well be certain aspects of one or another of the programs which would fit well into your own planning process. I know that you would be welcome to write or call any of these centers for further information.

We will try to keep on hand, in our Parish Nurse Resource Center, copies of any publications that are available which describe the activities of these programs.

> Parish Nurse Resource Center
> Parkside Center
> 1875 Dempster Street
> Park Ridge, IL 60068

MINISTER OF HEALTH PROGRAM OF IOWA LUTHERAN HOSPITAL, DES MOINES

GOALS, OBJECTIVES AND METHODOLOGY

GOAL

The goal of the Minister of Health Curriculum Pilot Project is to prepare professional nurses for ministry in congregations.

OBJECTIVES

The objectives of the Minister of Health Curriculum Pilot Project are to implement a three year training program beginning in 1986 which will (1) graduate six professional nurses by the end of each program year and (2) test a model of education for health ministry.

METHODOLOGY

The three-year project will encompass three program years and will prepare six nurses by the end of each year. The nurse trainees will enroll in the Clinical Pastoral Education Department at Iowa Lutheran Hospital. The nurse trainees will have an intensive three-week session at the beginning of the program when they will study and practice pastoral care concepts in a hospital setting under the direction of the Pastoral Services supervisor.

Following completion of this intensive session, nurses will move into the congregations for the internship experience under the direction of an internship supervisor, advisory committee made up of congregational members, and a liaison from the task force. The nurse trainee will assess health-related needs within the congregation and design appropriate methods to meet those needs within the context of health ministry. Throughout the internship experience, the nurse trainee will document experiences in a portfolio as evidence that curriculum expectations are being met.

Nurses will return to the hospital one day each week for seminars led by faculty and project directors of the Minister of Health Curriculum Pilot Project. These faculty will come from the rich resources of the hospital (nursing, family services, pastoral services and public relations), Lutheran Social Services, Grand View College, and other community agencies. The project directors will be Chaplain David F. Carlson, Head of the Department of Pastoral Services, and Dr. Jerry L. Schmalenberger, pastor of Saint John's Lutheran Church, Des Moines, Iowa.

Seminar topics will cover pastoral care, community nursing, wholistic health and wellness, social psychology, assertiveness training, and marketing and salesmanship skills. Because knowledge of community health nursing is so relevant to the Minister of Health role, each nurse trainee who has not previously completed a community health nursing course or had two years of supervised experience in a community health agency will be required to complete a course prior to or concurrently with the training program. The task force will assist nurses in locating such a course if necessary.

A certificate will be awarded to the nurse upon completion of the Minister of Health Curriculum.

Recruitment of nurse trainees will be the responsibility of the task force. Applications will be solicited through the news media, church publications, and recommendations of clergy. Each applicant will be interviewed and carefully screened for maturity and understanding of the role. Each nurse trainee selected must be a graduate of a state approved school of nursing, currently licensed as a Registered Nurse in the state of practice, and must have had two years of previous nursing experience. Each nurse trainee will be provided with a stipend during the taining program.

The task force will also be responsible for identifying congregations which will employ the nurse upon completion of the training program. In some instances, this may be the same as the internship congregation. Curriculum Project funding will provide assistance to the congregation for the nurse's salary for a limited time.

There are plans for ongoing publicity about the pilot project. A brochure will be developed which will be used to recruit students, internships, and employing congregations. News releases to the media and church publications, and journal articles will keep the public informed about this program and the role of the Minister of Health. Task force members and faculty plan to develop curriculum materials which will be available to others wishing to replicate the model, and will provide seminars and consultation as the need arises.

EVALUATION OF THE PROJECT

To effectively evaluate the Minister of Health Curriculum Pilot Project, several mechanisms have been designed.

1. Nurse trainees will provide ongoing oral feedback regarding curriculum and internship experience during seminars and informally. Written evaluations will be completed by students at the end of the program year.

59

2. Internship supervisors and advisory committees will provide verbal feedback to project directors and faculty throughout the program, and complete written evaluations at the end of the program year.

3. Faculty will informally evaluate the program throughout the year and file written evaluations at the completion of the year.

4. Progress of nurse trainees in meeting objectives of the curriculum will be determined through seminar discussions, portfolio evaluations, and conferences by liaison or project directors with internship supervisors and advisory committees.

5. During the second year of the project, feedback will be elicited from practicing nurses and employing congregations about the effectiveness of the learning experiences in the curriculum. In this way, faculty and project directors can gauge changes necessary in the curriculum and determine the accuracy of the job description.

Although not a part of this project, task force members hope to eventually secure funding for research. This research would evaluate the impact of the Minister of Health role on the health status of members of a congregation. The testing would be done by comparing congregations or by testing a congregation before placement of Minister of Health and again at the end of one, two, or three years with a Minister of Health on staff.

IOWA LUTHERAN HOSPITAL
CHARACTERISTICS/QUALIFICATIONS OF A PARISH NURSE

EDUCATION:

A registered professsional nurse with current nursing license, BSN or RN with active participation in continuing education programs relating to parish nurse responsibilities.

EXPERIENCE:

Three to five years nursing experience, preferably in one or more of the following areas: public health, education, public schools, medical/surgical nursing, and/or emergency room-outpatient nursing.

PERSONAL:

1. Knowledge of healing/health ministry of church.
2. Knowledge and practice of wholistic health philosophy.
3. Skill in communication and teaching techniques.
4. Knowledge in health promotion as it relates to life styles.
5. Knowledge of health services and resources in the community, including public health and hospice.
6. Motivated to grow personally and professionally.
7. Knowledge of current nursing and health care issues.
8. Participation in church and community activities which contribute to professional growth and to the promotion of wholistic health philosophy.
9. Knowledge and compliance to the Code of Ethics of Nursing and the Nurse Practice Act of Iowa.
10. Practice of confidentiality and professional standards.
11. Membership in professional organizations is encouraged.
12. Willingness to donate time as a Parish nurse for a year with the possibility that the church would consider the Parish nurse becoming a salaried person after a one-year pilot project.
13. Willingness to attend orientation sessions and/or an individualized self-study program.

Note: The feminine pronoun is used when referring to parish nurse in order to avoid the use of the awkward he/she phrase. This action does not mean to exclude the role of male nurses.

QUESTIONAIRE A
FOR CLERGY RESPONSE

Please check all responses which apply in each question.

1. In what ways do you think a Parish Nurse could be utilized in your congregation?

   ____ Personal health counselling   ____ Training health volunteers

   ____ Health education   ____ Health referrals

   ____ Screening clinics   ____ Other (please specify)

   ____ Visiting the sick

2. Do you think a Parish Nurse in your congregation could be utilized:

   ____ Frequently   ____ Seldom

   ____ Occasionally

3. Do you think your congregation would be willing to financially support the position:

   ____ Full-time   ____ 50% time

   ____ 75% time   ____ 25%

4. Do you think your congregation would be willing to share a Parish Nurse with another congregation?

   ____ Yes   ____ No

5. Should the Parish Nurse be:

   ____ a member of the congregation

   ____ not a member of the congregation

6. What salary should the Parish Nurse be paid?

7. Would your congregation be willing to provide an internship position (clinical experience for 9-12 months) for a Parish Nurse trainee?

   ____ Yes   ____ No

8. If your answer to #7 is "yes," do you think the congregation would be willing to furnish the Parish Nurse trainee with a stipend during the internship?

   ____ Yes   ____ No

9. Should the Parish Nurse internship occur in the same congregation which will provide employment upon completion of the program?

   ____ Yes   ____ No

10. Describe other support which your congregation might be willing to provide for the Parish Nurse intern.

11. What overlap of function do you think might occur between the pastor and nurse, or nurse and other staff members?

12. Describe content which you think is important to include in the Parish Nurse training program.

THANK YOU FOR YOUR INPUT!

Please tri-fold the questionnaire, staple and mail.

QUESTIONAIRE B
FOR NURSE RESPONSE

Please check all responses which apply in each question.

1. In what ways do you think a Parish Nurse could be utilized in your congregation?
   ___ Personal health counselling
   ___ Health education
   ___ Screening clinics
   ___ Visiting the sick
   ___ Training health volunteers
   ___ Health referrals
   ___ Other (please specify)

2. Do you think a Parish Nurse in your congregation could be be utilized:
   ___ Frequently   ___ Seldom
   ___ Occasionally

3. Would you be interested in becoming a Parish Nurse?
   ___ Yes   ___ No

4. If the answer to #3 above is "yes," would you be willing to participate in a 9-12 month training program combining seminars and clinical experiences:
   ___ on a full-time basis   ___ part-time only

5. If you are currently employed, would it be necessary for you to continue part-time employment during the training program?
   ___ Yes   ___ No

6. Would you prefer the clinical experiences:
   ___ in Des Moines   ___ in the congregation where you
   ___ in your home area   will be employed

7. If you were to enter the training program, would you be able to attend a full-time intensive session at the beginning of the program?
   ___ For one week   ___ For three weeks
   ___ For two weeks   ___ Other (specify)

8. How many days per week would you be able to take part in seminars and additional supervised clinical in Des Moines?
   ___ One   ___ Three
   ___ Two   ___ Four

9. When would be the best time for you to attend the seminars?
   ___ Weekdays daytime   ___ Week-end days
   ___ Weekday evenings

10. If you have not had a community health nursing course or community health nursing experience, would you prefer to take a course:
    ___ in Des Moines   ___ prior to entering the program
    ___ in your home community   ___ concurrent with the
                                     program

11. Describe content which you think is important to include in the Parish Nurse training program.

    THANK YOU FOR YOUR INPUT!

    Please tri-fold the questionnaire, staple and mail.

IOWA LUTHERAN HOSPITAL
MINISTER OF HEALTH EDUCATION PROGRAM

A LETTER OF UNDERSTANDING

The purpose of this Letter of Understanding is to articulate and document the agreements entered into by Iowa Lutheran Hospital's Pastoral Services Department's MINISTER OF HEALTH EDUCATION PROGRAM and this congregation and this Minister of Health Candidate:

EMPLOYING CONGREGATION	EMPLOYED MINISTER OF HEALTH CANDIDATE
_____	_____
Congregation	Name
_____	_____
Address	Address
_____	_____
City State Zip	City State Zip
_____	_____
Telephone	Telephone
_____	_____
Pastor/Supervisor	R.N. Lic. No.

1. The Minister of Health Education Program is a one year (12 months) educational internship designed to prepare qualifying participants to engage in the development of wholistic health ministeries in the congregation and community by functioning as a Minister of Health on the pastoral leadership team of this congregation. (For the first three weeks of training, which is full-time at the hospital, the Program will provide free room for those commuting great distances, and cover the costs of morning and evening meals.)

2. The term of this internship is one year beginning August 18, 1986 thru August 14, 1987. This congregation may choose to commit for additional one year internships; or may choose to employ a Minister of Health following this year; or both; or may discontinue any involvement with this program after one year. No commitment beyond this above stated year in implied.

3. The congregation, the candidate, or representatives of the Minister of Health Education Program may terminate this Letter of Understanding by a written notice of thirty (30) days to the other two parties.

4. The Minister of Health Program will provide a yearly stipend (grant) of $7,500.00 for this one year period, paid in 12 monthly payments. Taxes and Social Security deductions are not withheld by the Program, but are the responsibility of the individual candidate. This stipend will be reported as "other income" by an IRS Form 1099.

5. The congregation will provide a yearly salary of $2,500.00 for a total salary compensation of $10,000.00 for this twelve month year. Federal and State taxes will be withheld by the congregation on this salary of $2,500.00.

6. The congregation will be responsible for the following expenses, in addition to the above salary:

   a. Monthly travel allowance of $_____ or _____ ¢ per mile.

   b. Social Security taxes based on salary of $2,500.00.

   c. Health Insurance, if offered, comparable to other part-time staff.

   d. (Optional) Retirement benefits, if offered, comparable to other part-time staff.

   e. (Optional) Tuition re-embursement to their Minister of Health candidate of $ _____ .

   f. Other: _____

   _____

7. The congregation and its pastoral and lay leadership will mutually support and encourage the development of this Minister of Health by providing/participating in pastoral supervision of the Minister of Health candidate, establishment of a Health Cabinet/Committee, and involvement in training, consultation and evaluation sessions of the Minister of Health Education Program.

8. The position of the Minister of Health as outlined in the Program Guidebook will be followed. The competencies of the Minister of Health will be evaluated weekly by the Pastoral Supervisor and monthly by the Health Cabinet/Committee. The monthly evaulations may be conducted together with a representative of the Minister of Health Education Program. Open communication and feedback is essential for this model of education.

9. The hours of service and education of the Minister of Health candidate will be based on a half-time position of twenty-five (25) hours (average) each week, to be planned and fulfilled in cooperation with the Pastoral Staff, the Health Cabinet/-Committee, and the Director of the Minister of Health Education Program. Vacation time of two weeks will be granted for this year, to be mutually arranged.

10. The Minister of Health candidate will be required to carry her/his own professional liability insurance as a Registered Nurse. The congregation may arrange to include this staff person along with the liability coverage it carries for other staff.

11. _____

_____

12. _____

_____

****

Pastor/Supervisor - signed	date	Minister of Health Candidate date
Council President	date	Program Director	date

PARISH NURSE

When I first began to talk with people about the parish nurse concept, the usual response was, "What a good idea — but what is it really?" or "How does it work?"

So, I will try to answer some of the who, what, when, where, and why aspects of the Parish Nurse program.

HOW DID IT START? WHO? I have begun formal hours on Tuesdays from 9:00 A.M. - 12:00 Noon — an exciting step after a process which began in December. In December I met with Jan Berg, RN, who has been a parish nurse at St. Luke Lutheran Church in Sioux City.

The major leader in promoting the parish nurse concept is Granger Westberg, an LCA pastor/chaplain. He has written many books and articles about wholistic health and the role of the pastors, nurses and other health professionals in ministering to the needs of individuals.

WHAT? As I mentioned in the last newsletter, my role as a health educator will be to assist members to increase their practice of wellness, to answer health questions and/or direct clients to the appropriate health resource. I will not be doing hands-on skilled nursing care (such as drawing blood) since public health nurses perform those types of services.

I have written four goals: (1) Develop an organized health ministry, (2) Teach health/wellness to clients or to groups and perform activities of a healing ministry, (3) Promote wholistic health philosophy and the parish nurse concept, (4) Evaluate if a parish nurse is effective in changing members health habits and determine if the parish nurse is utilized by members.

This program will hopefully *evolve* according to members input and needs. Some specific activities which I will start with are: talking with any group within the church to explain my role, meeting with the preschool children in our daycare program every Tuesday for 10-15 minutes, visiting or phoning members as directed by Pastor, keeping an accurate record of activities done, and continuing to explain the parish nurse role to health professionals and agencies in our community.

WHEN AND WHERE? Although I will be at the church only on Tuesday mornings, I will be available if Pastor informs me of a need. Members may also call me at home. My "office" will be in the resource room.

WHY? There are many reasons why a parish nurse could be beneficial. One reason is that in America we have a sickness, not a wellness, program. For example, insurance pays for illness, but not for prevention of illness. In addition, there is no doubt of the tremendous interrelationship of the mind, body and spirit. A parish nurse could assist individuals in a better understanding of this interrelationship.

I hope this has answered some questions about the parish nurse. I have written a detailed summary of this project which discusses wholistic health, reasons for a parish nurse, program proposal, and possible activities related to the four goals. This. summary is available to all members and copies are in the Narthex and church office.

REQUESTS You knew it — eventually I would ask for something! Yes, I have three requests.

First, ask questions. Since no concrete guildelines, policies have been developed, your questions/concerns will assist me in writing a specific job description, policies, etc.

Second, I ask for your patience and understanding as the program develops. I certainly do not have all the answers about the program. Also, I will not have "pat answers" to all of your health questions. Hopefully, I will be able to answer many of your questions and/or direct you to a person or resource who can assist you. I do believe in helping persons to assume more responsibility and to learn more about their physical, emotional, and spiritual health. I feel it is essential for persons to have regular physician exams as well as to visit the physician when health problems are present. We — all health care professionals, pastors, and individuals — shoud be partners striving to improve the quality of life!

My third request is that I hope you will participate in health programs that are offered and visit or call me about health concerns!!

To paraphrase a title from a book by Jess Lair — "I may not know exactly where I'm going, but I'm sure not lost!"

Your Parish Nurse

Jan Striepe, RN

NORTHWEST IOWA PARISH NURSE NEWS

Needs, service, and growth . . . these words describe the parish nurse programs in Northwest Iowa. One year ago, in 1985, two churches had parish nurses. Today there are eleven churches with parish nurses.

In Sioux City the Wholistic Health Center, St. Luke's Regional Medical Center and Burlington Northern have supplied the necessary guidance and monetary support to establish the network of parish nurses. Jan Berg, a parish nurse since 1984, serves as the urban parish nurse coordinator. The registered nurses from the nine churches in the Sioux City area meet monthly to share project ideas and concerns, as well as having regularly scheduled speakers on a variety of health topics. The nurses work at least four hours a week at their churches and have focused on various health activities.

In the rural area of Clay county there are two parish nurse programs. Trinity Lutheran Church, Spencer, with Jan Striepe stresses wholistic health adult classes and programs on women's health issues while Bethlehem Lutheran Church in Royal, with Julie Christenson, gives particular attention to health maintenance of the elderly.

The Lutheran Brotherhood Foundation of Minneapolis gave Jan Striepe a grant to present seminars about the parish nurse concept. The presentations have increased the awareness and interest of both nurses and clergy about the concept. In addition, the grant provided funds to compile a booklet about implementing the parish nurse program in a rural area.

The project goal is to establish a network of ten parish nurse programs in a rural nine-county area. The nurses will receive a small stipend for attending orientation classes. Although the grant does not provide parish nurse salaries, it is hoped that the nurses will either be salaried by the church or volunteer their time.

Commenting on the progress made in Iowa, Dr. Mark Laaser, pastoral counselor at the Wholistic Health center stated, "We all know there is a rural health care crisis. Many small town hospitals have been forced to close. And, when they close the physician usually goes next." Laaser added, "All of these little towns still have a church. This could be very important in rural health care. For instance, there are over 1000 United Methodist churches in 600 towns in this state. Between the Lutherans, Catholics, and Methodists, we'd probably have every town covered."

Over all, there seems to be no doubt that parish nurses, whether urban or rural, paid or volunteer, are an enhancement to the church's ministry and the health care of a community.

COLUMBUS-CUNEO-CABRINI MEDICAL CENTER
HOSPITAL-PARISH HEALTH PROGRAM
A PROPOSAL

PURPOSE: in response to the Gospels and to the mission of the Missionary Sisters of the Sacred Heart, to extend the Medical Center's health care resources to the poor, the aged and migrant in a program that links the healing ministries of hospital and local church.

OVERVIEW: The Hospital-Parish Health Program (or Parish Nurse Program) proposes to recruit, place and support nurses on the staffs of six churches in the immediate areas of Columbus, Cuneo and Cabrini Hospitals, for a pilot period of two years. The work of this program is to address community health needs, especially those of the poor, in a preventive and educational way; and to do so in a cooperative way with the local parishes.

The parish nurse's ministry would be as an educator whose teaching promotes health, and as a skilled guide to parish members who care for the sick in various voluntary ways. The nurse would not be a substitute for medical treatment but rather she/he would be an informed source of referral to medical professionals when that need arises. Columbus, Cuneo and Cabrini Hospitals would offer six churches in this area the services of six nurses to work as professional members of their pastoral staff. Each parish will have special health care needs which will be recognized and addressed as the program develops and matures. But some needs are certainly predictable, such as:

A. Health, hygiene and nutrition education programs and consultation for teachers and children in the Parish schools.

B. Educational and screening programs for the older members of the community.

C. Skilled guidance and support of families with chronically ill members in their home.

D. Training and professional support of the various church groups who already provide spiritual, social, and emotional care of the sick of the parish.

E. Programs focused on the special needs of pregnant women, the bereaved, and families with young children.

There may well be patient referrals and ancillary benefits to our Hospitals deriving from sponsorships of the Parish Nurse Program. But the core rationale for commitment to this ministry derives from our Sponsor and Corporate missions, and from the

70

unique opportunity to continue in the inner city the healing ministry of the Missionary Sisters.

PROGRAM STRUCTURE AND ORGANIZATION

The Parish Nurse:

Duties: Health coordinator, counselor, coordinator and teacher of the volunteers, and coordinator of parish health-related programs.

Hours: On a half-time basis, or 20 hours per week.

Salary: $12,000 plus benefits

Qualifications: Candidates for the parish nurse program would be fully qualified professionally, with appropriate health care experience, have remained current in advanced nursing practices, be spiritually and emotionally mature and stable, committed to health care as a Christian vocation, as well as a personal career, and be willing and able to participate fully in all aspects of the parish nurse program. The nurse would be screened by the hospital for professional credentials and then interviewed and approved by both the relevant hospital staff and the responsible members of the parish staff.

The Hospital: The hospitals would provide half day per week educational and support programming for the six parish nurses at the hospital. This would include weekly consultation with relevant medical and nursing personnel, education and training in community health, in pastoral care, counseling, the theology of health ministry, and weekly group discussion of their experiences in the parish. Other professional hospital personnel would be available to them for educational programs or consultation on specific problems. The hospital may over time be asked to provide special support for programs in the parish such as health screening programs, lecturers, consultation, and referral to hospital based professionals and facilities.

The Parish: Each Parish will be expected to integrate the nurse into its pastoral team and ministry. Office space is to be provided and some program-related expenses covered. The pastor must be well-informed and cooperative. Although the hospital is paying the nurse, it is the individual church which the nurse services.

Program Management: The program will be managed through the Mission Effectiveness Office. On a day-to-day basis, it will be started up and coordinated by a half-time coordinator who will develop a Steering Committee and educational resources to the nurses.

Program Costs:

Parish Nurses (six)	$86,400 (Salary + Benefits)
Program Coordinator	$14,400 (Salary + Benefits)

Operating Costs (transportation costs of coordinators and RNs, educational materials) $10,000

Total $110,800

COLUMBUS-CUNEO-CABRINI MEDICAL CENTER
PARISH NURSE JOB DESCRIPTION

Position Title Parish Nurse

Position Relationships

Reports to Parish staff
Reports to Program Director

Value/Mission of Position

This position was created as a ministry of the church with the understanding that the Church's ministry of healing belongs to both the hospital and parish and the community they serve.

The person filling this position will embody this concept in their nursing care and ministry in the parish.

It is also understood that for many reasons, persons residing within the city of Chicago do not receive medical care through the hospital/clinic system of care. With the parish becoming a more visible center of healing, many persons previously unable or unwilling to use the hospital/clinic system may find experienced health care education, consultation and referrals through the ministry of the Parish Nurse.

The Parish Nurse will present a new type of "grass-roots" medical care for the community which will stress health maintenance and sickness prevention using wholistic concepts of health.

Position Overview

This position is designed to provide leadership in identifying and meeting the health education and counseling needs of the members of the congregation of the participating parish.

Principal Duties and Responsibilities

1. The Parish Nurse is expected to play a highly visible role in the life and activities of the congregation. This includes involvement as follows:

   a. Prepares and teaches or co-ordinates courses and/or seminars to the congregation and community on health maintenance, disease prevention and early detection through screening.

   b. Acts as a personal health counselor to members of the congregation and community which includes:
   — Assessing health problems.
   — Recommending and/or providing minor treatment and/or first aid.
   — Referring to physician and/or community support services, if needed.
   — Educating and communicating good health concepts.

2. Participates as a full staff member of the parish team, attending staff meetings and making/accepting referrals within this group.

3. Provides feedback to the program director and other nurses regarding recommendations for change in the program.

4. Maintains records required by the parish and/or program director for program evaluation.

5. Co-ordinates a cadre of volunteers who will assist in meeting the goals of the program.

6. Participates in weekly program where will meet with program director, program nurses and faculty for mutual support, continuing education and program planning.

Knowledge, Skills and Qualities Required

1. Licensed in State of Illinois as R.N.
2. Community/Public Health experience
3. Medical/Surgical experience
4. Participation in health education programs
5. Commitment to wellness promotion as a special ministry
6. Counseling skills desired
7. Faith commitment
8. Bi-lingual/bi-cultural abilities for three predominantly hispanic parishes. These capabilities desirable for other three parishes.

73

In general, the Parish Nurse Job Description embodies four areas of Nursing Ministry.

1. Health Educator
2. Health Counselor
3. Co-ordinator of Volunteers
4. Source of Referrals

AGREEMENT BETWEEN
LUTHERAN GENERAL HOSPITAL, INC.
and

_____

THIS AGREEMENT is entered into this _____ day of
_____, 1985 between _____
hereinafter referred to as "Parish" and LUTHERAN GENERAL
HOSPITAL, INC., hereinafter referred to as "LGH."

WITNESSETH

WHEREAS, LGH and Parish desire to enter into an agreement
whereby LGH will provide a Parish Nurse to Parish on a part-time
basis;

WHEREAS, LGH provides health care services which include
the services of professional nurses;

WHEREAS, Parish is a church seeking to meet the needs of its
congregation and to fulfill its spiritual commitment which includes
assisting with physical, emotional, and spiritual aspects of health
care;

NOW, THEREFORE, in consideration of the mutual covenants,
obligations and agreements set forth herein the parties agree as
follows:

DEFINITIONS:

PROJECT. The term "project" refers to the plan formulated by
LGH and several churches to place nurses on the staffs of
several churches in the Chicagoland area.

PARISH NURSE. The term "Parish Nurse" refers to the registered nurse providing health care services to the
Parish/congregation.

I. TERM

.1 This Agreement shall be effective as of _____ , 1985,
for a term of three years subject, however, to prior termina-
tion as hereinafter provided.

II. TERMINATION

2.1 Either party may terminate this Agreement, with or without
cause, at any time with sixty days prior written notice to the
other party.

III. OBLIGATIONS OF THE PARTIES

3.1 LGH agrees:

a) To provide a Parish Nurse in consultation with the Parish on a half-time basis, or twenty hours per week, whose work shall be performed in accordance with the job description attached hereto and incorporated herein as Exhibit 1.

b) To sponsor continuing education to Parish Nurses as needed.

c) To provide professional liability insurance coverage ($1,000,000 per occurrence limit) with respect to the professional activities of Parish Nurses who are LGH personnel and to provide written endorsement of such coverage evidenced by a Certificate of Insurance to the Parish.

d) To provide salary and benefits to Parish Nurses who are LGH personnel, which shall include all those supplemental benefits offered by LGH to hospital based part-time employees.

e) To reimburse the nurse for travel expenses to meetings and continuing educational programs at LGH in accord with LGH policy.

3.2 Parish agrees:

a) To provide the facilities, furnishings, educational materials and equipment as may be required at the Parish by the Parish Nurse.

b) To provide secretarial support from the Parish's secretarial office as may be required by the Parish Nurse.

c) To participate in the selection process of the Parish Nurse.

d) To form a Health Committee to assist the steering committee in coordinating the work of the Parish Nurse.

e) To reimburse the nurse for travel expenses within the Parish community in accord with Parish policy.

IV. GENERAL COVENANTS AND CONDITIONS

4.1 Payment

Parish shall pay LGH for the services of Parish Nurse in the amounts set forth as follows:

i. The first year: Parish shall pay LGH a minimum of $2,500 for the Parish Nurse's services in three equal installments, the first installment to be paid by the end of the first month, the second installment to be paid by the end of the fourth month, and the third install-ment to be paid at the end of the eighth month.

ii. The second year: Parish will pay LGH a minimum of $5,000 for the Parish Nurse's services in installments as set forth in i.

iii. The third year: Parish will pay LGH a minimum of $7,500 for the Parish Nurse's services in installments as set forth in i.

4.2 Records

All records created and maintained by the Parish Nurse shall be the property of LGH. These records shall be considered confidential. LGH and Parish agree to comply with applicable LGH policies and procedures, and all applicable state and federal laws, rules and regulations governing the release of these records.

4.3 Personnel Policies

The Parish Nurse, as an LGH employee, shall be subject to LGH personnel policies regarding her employment.

4.4 Steering Committee

A steering committee shall be formed to oversee the project and assure its mission, quality and effectiveness by performing the following functions:

a) To maintain liaison among the hospital, project staff, the Parish Nurse, the Health Committee, and the Parish to assure that the project is operational.

b) To assess the project's value, consistency with concept, effectiveness and future growth and to make those changes deemed necessary for a fuller implementation.

c) To develop means and resources to establish, evaluate, maintain and measure the nurse's unique role as health educator and counselor.

d) The membership of the steering committee may include but shall not be limited to:

   i.   Chairman of Pastoral Care or designee

   ii.   V.P. of Nursing Services or designee

   iii. Primary care physician

   iv.   Hospital Administrator or designee

   v.   Legal Counsel

   vi.   Project Director

   vii. Parish Pastor or designee

4.5 Compliance With Laws

All parties shall comply with all the requirements of county, municipal, state, federal and other applicable governmental authorities, now in force or which may thereafter be in force pertaining to the performance of this agreement, and shall faithfully observe all municipal and county ordinances, state and federal statutes now in force or which may thereafter be in force.

4.6 Notice

All notices required to be served by provisions of this Agreement may be served on any of the parties hereto personally or may be served by sending a letter duly addressed by certified or registered mail. Notices to be served on LGH shall be served at or mailed to

_____

_____ unless otherwise instructed. Notice be served on Parish shall be serviced at or mailed to _____

_____ unless otherwise instructed.

4.7 Inclusion of All Terms and Conditions in Writing

This Agreement embodies the whole agreement of the parties. There are no promises, terms, conditions or obligations other than those contained herein and this Agreement shall supersede all previous communications, representations, or agreements, either verbal or written, between the parties hereto.

4.8 Written Modification

This Agreement may be modified at any time in writing by mutual agreement of the parties.

_____
For LGH

_____
For Parish

Date _____

Granger Westberg
Director
Parish Nurse Project

Jill Westberg McNamara
Editorial Assistant

Granger E. Westberg is a pioneer in the relationship of religion and medicine. He is adjunct clinical professor, department of Preventive Medicine and Community Health at the University of Illinois, College of Medicine.

In 1973 he was the founder and director of Wholistic Health Centers, Inc. These are experimental medical clinics where physicians, nurses and clergy combine their efforts in whole-person care, with special concern for the spiritual dimensions of illness and health.

He is the author of several books including the classic "Good Grief" —a constructive approach to the problem of loss — which is in its twenty-third printing, totaling a million copies. He is a consultant to a growing number of hospitals and churches showing interest in the Parish Nurse concept. He sees the possibility of congregations playing an increasingly important role in keeping people healthy at the level of prevention and personal motivation.

Jill Westberg McNamara has been active in the wholistic health center movement since her college days when she worked as a part-time research assistant in the office of the Wholistic Health Centers in Hinsdale, Illinois. She and the pastor of the church she attended developed the idea of a Health Cabinet to stimulate interest in a whole-person approach to Christian ministry. In 1980 she wrote the booklet "How to Start a Health Cabinet in your Church." Over a thousand congregations have responded to the suggestions of this manual.

Until the coming of her first child she served for three years on the staff of the Evangelical Hospital System in Oakbrook, Illinois in the office of the vice-president for religion and health.